EKCO

SOUNDS

HOW A SOUTHEND RADIO MAKER CHANGED THE WORLD

CHRIS POOLE & PETER C BROWN

ESTUARYPUBLISHING

First published in December 2013

Estuary Publishing

www.estuarypublishing.co.uk

ISBN 978-0-9570635-3-2

Printed in the UK by Clays Ltd, Elcograf S.p.A.

In Memory of Chris Poole

Aknowledgements

My sincerest thanks to the following people, without whose invaluable contributions and support, this book could not have been written:

John Brown, Ella Chadwick, Derek Cole, Dave Gibbings, Rose Henstridge, Bob Hubbard, Geoff Meredith, Pam O'Flynn, David Parsons, Chris Poole, Dave Smith, Pete Terry, and Dave Wiggins.

Thanks too to Audrey Snee, the publisher, who had the onerous task of editing the work, for her tireless patience and sensitivity.

A special thanks also to Ian Mcmahon for his assistance with the records and files of his uncle, the late Chris Poole, in order for this book to be written, thus ensuring that his diligent work, carried out over more than two decades, about Eric Cole and the extraordinary company he built, can be realised in print.

I feel sure that you would like this Chris.

Peter C Brown, December 2013

Contents

A T THE TURN of the 20th century, an exciting new invention had everyone transfixed. The radio brought the world into people's homes and for young Eric Kirkham Cole it was a chance to experiment, as he built 'Cat's Whiskers' radio devices at his parents' kitchen table. Never could he have imagined then how his unique talent would be used to defend Britain from Nazi invasion, nor how his small radio set business which he set up in his garden shed in 1922 - the same year the British Broadcasting Corporation (BBC) was formed - would become a global brand designing the must-have gadgets of the day.

From radios with station dials, car radios, convection heating, fluorescent lighting, to the first genuine portable television, E.K.Cole Ltd (EKCO) dominated the market for over four decades. EKCO is less known for its role in the birth of radar, developing tactical radar for the V-bombers, ground-breaking military and civilian airport and airborne radar systems, as well as vital equipment for the medical and nuclear industries. EKCO even provided the technology behind Britain's first guided missile. Subsidiary EKCO factories carried out secret manufacturing work for the British government during the Second World War and it has recently been revealed that EKCO modified radios to be used as listening devices for Bletchley Park before the Enigma machine was obtained, and that EKCO employees were so highly skilled, many were employed on the Enigma monitoring duties.

Eric took the same pioneering ethos to his workforce, and his company was one of the first in Britain to introduce paid holidays, occupational pension schemes, and an employee social and sports club which still exists today. In its heyday, EKCO was the largest employer in Southend, employing over 7,000 people. It was said that if you met somebody in Southend High Street it was an odds-on bet that this person either worked for the company, was related to someone who worked for EKCO, or knew somebody who did.

This book, with narrative by Eric's son, Derek Cole, and many former employees, reveals not only the history of this great Essex company from 1924 to its sudden takeover in 1966, but the passion and talent of the people who once worked there. EKCO was much more than just a radio factory.

Chapter 1

Formation Of An Iconic Company

The EKCO company produced some of the best loved iconic gadgets of the 20th century from the round radio designed by Wells Coates in 1934, the sleek-design television in 1938, the 'Radiotime' alarm clock (also designed by Wells Coates) in 1946, to the portable television in 1955.

In early 1958, the one millionth EKCO-Vision television set came off the production line at the EKCO works in Priory Crescent to a great fanfare, as it was ceremonially presented to the Sunshine Children's home in Shoeburyness. This event represented the pinnacle of the ever-increasing push towards a production target of 5,000 television sets a week. The zealous drive of its founder is what made the EKCO company so successful, but ultimately led to its demise.

Eric Cole was born in Southend on 4 July 1901. He was the only son of Henry and Alice Laura Cole, and lived at 2, Beedell Avenue. His unusual middle name 'Kirkham' was actually his mother's maiden name. His father was a dairyman who had a small but thriving business, although later he sold it to the Clement family (who owned and ran Howards Dairies) in order to finance a change of career to electrical contractor, setting up in business as 'Henry Cole Electrical Contractor'. Eric was remembered by his peers as having an inquisitive mind. He completed his education at Hamlet School in Westcliff and then attended the Southend Technical College. His neighbours recall how he was 'always experimenting,' and his 1915 college wireless textbooks sat on his bookshelf for many years to come. The widespread comment was that he had 'the electronic equivalent of green fingers'.

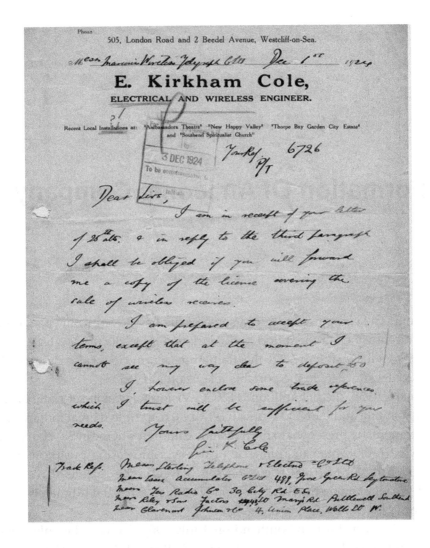

A letter from Eric Cole in response to Marconi's patent infringement claim, dated 1st December 1924.

"In reply to the third paragraph, I shall be obliged if you will forward me a copy of the license covering the sale of wireless receivers. I am prepared to accept your terms, except at the moment I cannot see my way clear to deposit £80. I however enclose trade references which I trust will be sufficient for your needs."

Upon leaving college, Eric began working with his father wiring houses; it was a time when electricity was still being introduced to domestic properties. In 1920, the business name changed to 'Henry Cole and Son Electrical Engineers' which traded from a workshop behind the family home in Beedell Avenue. They were awarded a contract by the Southend Estate Company, which was building property steadily eastwards along the seafront towards Thorpe Bay. Two years later, the business name was changed again to 'Eric Cole – Electrical Engineer,' as Eric pursued his interest in radio.

The British Broadcasting Company (BBC) and Marconi (which had been making its own transmissions since their broadcast of 'three little clicks' bridged the Atlantic in 1901) had started broadcasting. In addition to building sets, there were always radios to repair as well as a battery charging service (these were called accumulators in those days) since most radio sets were battery powered because of the wide variance in electricity supply. The national grid at 240 volts AC (Alternating Current) was not agreed until 1926, and DC (Direct Current) was still commonplace. Southend at that time had 230 volts DC. The big change in the business came in late 1923, when the builders of a major Southend cinema went bust, leaving their materials suppliers, including EKCO, unpaid.

Eric was left with only the radio business to concentrate on, but was unaware that in building his radio sets, he was unwittingly infringing certain patents of the Marconi Wireless Company. In late 1924, Marconi opened correspondence with him, seeking reimbursement for the use of their patents.

The future for Eric didn't look so bright. Then one of his customers, William 'Billy' Streatfield Verrells, suggested he make his radios work from the lighting mains, rather than run them off accumulators. Verrells, who at that time was a schoolteacher, was exasperated that the accumulator in his radio had let him down in the middle of an interesting program. He complained to Eric that as an electrician, he should be able to make his wireless work from the lighting mains, which at that time was on DC. Eric replied that 230 volts was too powerful to run a 6-volt set and apart from the danger of fire, the reception would be drowned by interference. Nevertheless, later that evening in his workshop, Eric, thinking about Verrells' comments, rigged up a series of lamps between the set and the mains, which reduced the voltage to the required 6 volts and while the set worked, the hum was awful. After reading through textbooks, he inserted a high-capacity condenser to smooth out the hum and took this contraption around to Verrells, who was delighted even though he still needed his high-tension battery and the glare and heat from the electric lamps was pretty bad.

Determined to improve on this, Eric substituted a resistance for the electric lamps. However this became very hot and needed a metal case to avoid the risk of fire. Eric later told one of his managers that it was so hot he could have fried eggs on it! Eric persevered and improved the apparatus and even sold a few to his friends locally. He later succeeded in incorporating into 'his brainchild' a device, which also supplied the high-tension current, hitherto needing a high tension (HT) battery.

The company came into being when Verrells persuaded Eric to advertise his contraption in the radio journals. Although, the device was still crude and not in accordance with the regulations of the Institute of Electrical Engineers covering mains devices, there was a rapid rise in sales with the result that they went into partnership, using Eric Cole's initials as a trade mark, thus becoming E K Cole Ltd. It was the start of a formidable partnership that went on to create a company that would not only become the biggest employer in Southend-on-Sea, but a world-leader in global electronics. It was life changing for both men.

Derek Cole credits his father's success to his unusual combination of qualities and the very talented people he worked with.

"My father had an astonishing talent for innovation, spotting at great speed what the future would need. The battery eliminator was the first of many and his initial partner, Billy Verrells, also had this talent for innovation and between them they spotted the need to connect the wireless to the mains. He was well known as an outstanding wireless engineer for the first part of the 20th century, although he always credited this to the legendary Mickey Finn at Southend Technical College.

"My father actually dated my mother by wireless radio. This seems to anticipate the concept of the mobile phone! Such private transmissions were in fact a breach of the Post Office monopoly under the Telegraphy Act. This was passed before the telephone, let alone the wireless, was invented, and in later years EKCO was meticulous in only broadcasting under licence."

Verrells was born in Sevenoaks Kent in 1893, and by the early 1900s the family had moved to East London. After having a lung removed in a Swiss sanatorium because of tuberculosis, he was advised to find a job involving some open air, and moved to Southend where the sea air was reputed to be good for the lungs.

With the formation of the company, Verrells (who had since left the teaching profession) became the chairman and managing director, with Eric appointed as the works and technical director – giving him the freedom to be the 'ideas man' to develop the business. Running the commercial activity gave Verrells a new lease of life, as he discovered a keen commercial sense, and he took charge of commercial policy as well as employing sales and publicity staff. Capital came from John Maxwell, who owned and ran the 'Peter Pan Playground' (a well-known local amusement park on the Southend seafront); Henry Manners (an enterprising local builder); and Ernest Pring (a local milkman) - all of whom became directors of the company. Derek Cole has vivid memories of each of his father's colleagues.

"My maternal grandmother, Sally Bradshaw, let her flat over her sweetshop at the north end of Hamlet Court Road be used by her future son-in-law as an ad-hoc crystal set factory in the very early days. She was a very live wire, and almost certainly responsible for her brother, Richard Godsill's role as the first 'EKCO dealer'. Billy Verrells had developed the technique of spotting houses with wireless aerials, which were needed to receive a signal at the time. He would then knock on the door to sell eliminators.[1] Billy was an ebullient honorary uncle throughout our childhood and on at least two occasions shared our family holiday at the Ocean Hotel, Sandown, with his second wife, Ivy, and her children. But it was Ernie Pring who was the most consistent and long serving of all of my father's colleagues. He walked into the workshop in 1926 with a cheque for £1,000, saying: 'I want a share in your business,' triggering the formation of the private company. With the depression coming, it was about the only successful investment Pring ever made.

"Maxwell, Manners and Pring also owned the hire boats on the Serpentine. I never knew Maxwell, but Henry Manners is credited with saving my life when he found me dangling by straps from my pram. My mother's cash books show substantial payments were made to his company, as my father was a major investor in the Manners Way Estate. Derek Gardens is named after me. Henry became regular a visitor after the war. He was great fun and we looked forward to his visits. My sister and I had become ruthless players of croquet, a situation he accepted with great good humour."

---

[1] *Richard Godsill did the same on his extensive official rounds in Liverpool, where he was the Relieving Officer (Director of Social Services) and the expert on transforming the Elizabethan Poor Law into the new system abolishing the Work House under Lloyd George's famous People's Budget of 1911. He was so successful that he was loaned to Birmingham to repeat his work there.*

The partnership between Verrells and Cole not only helped them create and run a large and enterprising business, but also saw them become engaged as property developers in Southend. During the 1930s, the pair were instrumental in building what is now known as 'The Somerset Estate', which lies off Prince Avenue, Southend. Now that he had a viable business, Eric took the opportunity to marry his girlfriend Muriel Bradshaw in 1925. Muriel subsequently joined the staff as book keeper and personnel manager, and secretary to the chairman. The EKCO business name was adopted in 1926 when E K Cole Ltd was formally incorporated. Although a successful decision at the time, it was considered later on to be an unwise one, according to Derek.

"My father insisted that all five shareholders should have an equal share. Long afterwards the financier, Sir John Keeling, said to him, 'You cheated yourself out of your birth right.' After he left EKCO, my father told me, 'If I get involved in anything else, I will keep control.'"

An original Battery Eliminator   (D.Cole)

As most of England at the time was supplied with alternating current (AC), the company's sales were limited to those areas still on direct current (DC) and it was soon evident that they would have to produce a model of an 'eliminator' that was usable on AC current. However, this involved more technical knowledge than Eric possessed as an electrician. He sought the assistance of people who made rectifiers and condensers and managed to produce a model usable on AC. It was a crude apparatus but sales of the units were higher than expected. He had the foresight to realise that as mains powered radio sets came onto the market (following the adoption of the National Grid), eliminator sales would fade out so production was turned over to making mains powered radio sets, which had two and three-valve sets (without speakers) using the new indirectly heated valves. These new receivers were rather unreliable - not unexpectedly - since the technology was new and reliable components were unavailable. As the first actual receivers they produced, the design was somewhat experimental, but again the demand for the sets was high and they sold well. As the business expanded, so did the factory size; first moving to larger premises at 505, London Road, Leigh-on-Sea, and shortly afterwards relocating to number 513.

Chapter 2

The Formative Years and Expansion

Such was the early success of EKCO, within three years of being formed the company had commissioned a purpose built factory located at 1135, London Road, Leigh-on-Sea. It was a testament to the ambition of its founder Eric Cole, who sought to employ a large team of professional engineers to design more functional, reliable and much safer products.

1135 London Road, Leigh-on-Sea (C.Poole,)

This recruitment programme (which ran between 1928-9) was the cornerstone of the company's subsequent commercial success. He recruited technical staff who had previously worked for firms such as Marconi, His Master's Voice (HMV), and Kolster-Brandes Ltd (an American owned manufacturer of radio and television sets based in Kent). They were employed as much for their technical skills as their experience in volume production. John Wyborn, who was poached from HMV, was appointed EKCO's chief engineer; while the chief of testing Norman Robertson and his deputy, John Harbour, were recruited from Kolster-Brandes.

At the same time, Eric recognised the need for 'home-grown' talent, so he began to recruit bright school leavers who showed an aptitude for electronics to work alongside the professional engineers. Among these were two young lads, Jack Gard and Ted O'Flynn, both of whom were to play a predominant role in radar development from 1939.

Yet the most eminent recruit of the 1928-9 recruitment programme was Tony Martin, whom Eric discovered working as a garage hand at a dealership on the south coast, and who seemed to know more about EKCO products than the boss himself. Even though he had no academic training, Tony was destined to become the leading figure in the design of the wartime design of airborne radar equipment.

Derek Cole:
"In 1929, a new wireless did not work well south of the Surrey Downs and my father worked out some improved circuitry, put a few components in his car and set out to visit dissatisfied customers. At Tony's home, he was told, 'He is working at the village petrol pump.' There, he found a young man filling cars but when he explained his purpose, Tony replied, 'Don't worry, I've fixed it'. Back at Tony's home he found the set working perfectly with circuitry he had not thought of, so he offered Tony a job in the EKCO lab. Sixteen years later this led to the award to Tony of an MBE for his work over the whole range of EKCO radar and other electronic products."

Another of Eric's key recruits was Richard Spencer, who would go on to become an essential member of the research and development team. Spencer was recruited in 1929 from Marconi's by John Wyborn. He brought to the company his speciality subject of testing of all materials produced; life-testing of the factory's completed output before mass production was allowed to proceed and random tests on completed warehouse stocks to prevent faulty material getting to the customer. It was the strict procedures adopted by 'Spen',

Mr Richard "Spen" Spencer
(C.Poole)

as he was affectionately known, coupled with the skilled team around him which resulted in the esteemed reputation of EKCO radios and televisions for quality and reliability to last for more than 30 years with both the trade and the customers.

By 1929, with the rapid expansion of both battery eliminators and mains radios, there were about a hundred people working for the company. The company was becoming much more profitable (in excess of £30,000 per annum, which in those days was a veritable fortune) and with the new engineers setting the pace and standard, new designs for the sets were coming through. These were exhibited at the annual Radiolympia Show (held in London every August-September) and proved to be such a success that to keep pace with the demand it was decided that considerably larger premises were needed, with the scope for further expansion. As a result of this, a green field site (actually a cabbage patch) in Priory Crescent, Prittlewell, Southend, was acquired and work commenced on a completely new factory, built by a local company, 'Bentall Estates', which was owned by Mr Manners. In fact, in addition to building the factory, he went on to build a whole housing estate adjacent to the factory, which to this day is called the 'Manners Way Estate'. The construction of the 100,000 square feet factory was completed in 1930 and this was to remain the main headquarters and manufacturing site for the rest of the life of the company. Now that the company had sufficient space and the technical staff, rapid expansion took place and very soon there were around 500 people working for the company.

Ella Chadwick was employed at EKCO from 1929-1944 and recalls how fast the company grew.

"My time at EKCO started in 1929 when, having become fed up with seasonal work, I approached EKCO who took me on at their factory, which in those days was at 1135, London Road, Leigh-on-Sea. Joining a small production team numbering probably no more than fifty ladies, I was first taught to solder components using an iron which was kept hot by a small gas flame. Having learned the technique, my job was soldering leads into a smallish box, which I was told was a battery eliminator and was one of the company's best-selling products. I remember that the foreman was a chap called Mr Dudley. I was obviously deemed to be very proficient, because I was later moved upstairs to join a small team assembling and wiring up radios which were being developed by the experimental department. In 1930, we were moved to the new factory in Priory Crescent.

"At that time the company was considerably larger, yet the new assembly hall still seemed enormous. It was here that I first met Michael Lipman, who was setting up the production lines, and I remember that he was so enthusiastic, always running around moving this or that until he got things as he wanted them.

"Although battery eliminators were still being made, most of the production was concentrated on radio production, but as far as us ladies were concerned it was just another assembly job. As an hourly paid worker I was earning four (old) pence and three farthings an hour and working a 44-hour week, but by the end of 1931 I had become a Line Supervisor, which meant that I was salaried and on a weekly wage."

The 1929 American stock market crash set off a global economic meltdown and as British exports halved, unemployment in the UK rose to three million. But while the National Government of 1931 cut benefits of insured workers by ten percent, EKCO was again bucking the trend. It introduced unprecedented holidays with pay for its staff. The company's output was also on the rise.

The 1930s was an era of innovation in design and production, and EKCO introduced an expanding range of products. However, a major issue it faced was the high cost of the wooden radio cabinets, which were a major feature of the EKCO radio sets. Then in March 1930, Michael Lipman, who was a technical sales representative employed by AEG in Germany, made an appointment to see Mr Ratcliffe, the chief purchaser for EKCO, and showed him a Bakelite cabinet AEG made for the German company Telefunken. This newly invented Bakelite material, which was a type of plastic, was cheaper than veneered wood and could be used for most cabinets.

As Lipman later recalled: "Ratcliffe was looking for a new cabinet design and grabbed it. He took it upstairs and returned a few minutes later with John Wyborn, the chief engineer. After asking me a few questions, I was then whisked upstairs to the board room where I was introduced to Eric Cole and Billy Verrells. They were wildly excited about the cabinet and said that 'this was just what they needed to launch themselves into the radio-set market proper.' Within an hour, an inquiry was made for 30,000 cabinets of two designs and a request for a designer to come over from Berlin at once, as the new sets had to be ready for the annual Radiolympia Exhibition in August 1930. The order was duly placed and was the largest single order for Bakelite cabinets placed by a radio manufacturer at that time."

This bode well for Lipman as shortly afterwards EKCO offered him the job of production engineer for the new factory with responsibility for the installation and equipment of a tool room, machine shop and mass production assembly facilities. The new sets in their Bakelite cabinets were an instant success, as were the loudspeakers in cabinets to match - in those days the speakers were separate from the receivers, largely because the early valves were 'microphonic', i.e. they were affected by the speaker vibrations, which caused some distorted reception.

The AD65 model (DesignC20)

In early 1931, a fresh range of combined receivers and speakers was designed, again with Bakelite cabinets made initially in limited colours - black, mottled brown and mottled green (true Bakelite was brown and black because of the extreme heat it endured while being cured). The factory space had to be extended because the existing area was too small for production to meet projected output.

"In 1931, EKCO launched yet another brilliant idea," recalls Derek Cole. "Realising that the twiddling of numerous knobs and delicate tuning adjustments were beyond the ordinary housewife, they then produced a set that bore a scale marked with the names of the stations themselves. This sent the sales soaring - and was typical of the foresight and genius of the men who had founded the firm."

The sets cost 11 guineas, which is the equivalent to just over £600 today based on inflation adjusted pricing. And they still retain their high value as valuable iconic collector items. The AD65 is the most sought-after model.[1]

---

[1] A rare AD65 valve radio, circa 1934 was on sale for £1,000 in November 2013

Some ten assembly lines were built using the conveyor-belt technique that Lipman had seen in use at Ford's Dagenham plant, which he adapted for use on the radio lines. It allowed six models to be produced alongside each other.

It seemed EKCO could do no wrong, and a measure of the success of the company was the fact that within two years of moving to Priory Crescent, production had quadrupled and the number of people who were employed at the site reached a thousand.

The tremendous popularity of its radio products was reflected in the rapid extension of the 'Mobile Service' section of the EKCO radio division. In March 1931, a small army of five motor-cycle mechanics was introduced. The mobile service force quickly increased to thirty highly skilled engineers who travelled by motor cars and motor cycles to EKCO radio receiver owners in all parts of the country during the course of their weekly routine.

These 'Radio Doctors', as they were sometimes called, carried a complete set of tools, spare parts and equipment enabling them to repair almost everything on the spot. Under firm control of their enterprising service manager, the section maintained a high standard of efficiency.

1932 EKCO
service engineers

Despite its popularity, EKCO was not impervious to external factors. By 1931 the Great Depression was impacting the UK particularly severely. EKCO had no option but to reduce its retail prices by 15 percent in a year, and as a consequence wages were also cut by 10 percent. Despite the downturn, EKCO was floated on the Stock Exchange in September 1931, again defying the reigning financial chaos.

EKCO Bakelite presses (All images C.Poole)

Eric Cole and Billy Verrells went to Germany to suggest to AEG that their cabinets could be made in the UK by EKCO. They agreed that for an annual fee and a royalty, a factory would be erected by EKCO adjacent to the main plant, using presses supplied by AEG. This agreement was very onerous at the time, but following the issue of a share prospectus in December 1931, where new shares to the value of £400,000 were issued, the plastics factory was built and the future supply of cabinets was assured. The EKCO share issue was oversubscribed and, as reported in the *Financial Times*, 'no shares can compare with those of E K Cole and the success of the issue is all the more remarkable in the present difficult state of the markets and certainly reflects credit on all those concerned.'

The Bakelite Press Hall was under construction in March 1932. It was 100ft long, 63ft wide and 50ft high. The height was dictated by the fact that each of the three large presses stood 35ft high and there needed to be a 35-ton travelling crane running the entire length of the building in order to move the large press tolls around. The presses sat on concrete foundations which were 13½ feet deep and required 550 tons of concrete. The presses, made by Niederrheinische Maschinenfabrik Becker and van Hullen AG, Krefeld, were the largest in the country, the largest of which was 600 ton. A team of scientists and engineers came over to run the factory, and eventually the engineers returned home, leaving behind one chemist, Dr Willi Hahn, who by all accounts was a brilliant engineer (he returned to Germany in 1939 when war broke out). The initial object was to manufacture radio cabinets. In fact it was the beginning of the plastics industry in Britain.

In 1934, EKCO caused a sensation when it revealed its latest invention - the car radio. The company led the world market in design and installation. At first only the luxury car maker Rolls Royce fitted EKCO car radios as standard. Other car manufacturers were slow to follow as they believed car radios were unnecessary.

Chapter 3

Fire, Disaster and Recovery

EKCO published their first staff magazine called *'Echoes'* in May 1932. It had a subscription rate of tuppence a copy, 2/- per annum to members, or 2/6 per annum (post free) to members or friends in any part of the British Isles. It gave a very good snapshot of the company; in the first six years of existence, capital rose from £2,500 to £400,000, floor space increased from 50 square feet to 172,200 square feet and output (sales) soared from £1,000 to £1.25 million.

However, even as the debut magazine was being printed, there was a disastrous fire in the experimental department, which spread and also burned down the drawing office. The fire destroyed all the design data and models for the coming season (1932-3), and the engineering drawings necessary for production. It made headlines for the next issue.

On the Friday morning the staff arrived to find that fire had destroyed the offices, the experimental department, and penetrated into the service department, exposing a considerable portion of the factory to the open skies, but by the Tuesday morning of the following week, the staff was at work again, and the factory in full production. There was no time to re-design the new range, and EKCO had no choice but to persevere and build the two principal models for the season using the same basic chassis and in the same cabinets as for 1931.

From *'Echoes'* Staff Magazine 1932-3

Derek Cole was too young to remember it but it was a story often repeated in the family.

"My mother mainly remembered the factory fire of February 1932 because I was just cutting my teeth, and every time she got me to sleep another newspaper rang for news, which she could not give. The experimental department with most of the new models was destroyed. The *Southend Standard* reported that after three days, office routine had been restored with the executives working next to typists and clerks in a hastily cleared portion of the factory. In five days production was again in full swing and this won the admiration of leaders of industry throughout the country.

"The government had introduced high import duties in November 1931, sending the cost of bakelite cabinets, which could not be molded in Britain, through the roof. EKCO made an emergency share issue to finance the first major home Bakelite factory, but the *Southend Standard* reported in August 1932 that it was not yet ready. Outdated imported high cost cabinets had to be used for Radiolympia in September."

The company may have got itself back up and running quickly but it impacted severely on trade as it was expected the firm would produce something entirely new each year. Orders fell, and while production went ahead, it soon became apparent that there was a 50 percent drop in sales and a large stock of unsold sets built up. By January 1933, this brought about a financial crisis and the shares dropped on the London Stock Exchange as investors were reluctant to finance unsold stocks.

"The bank put in an administrator and my father often recalled the huge risk he and Billy Verrells took. They purchased the shares owned by Manners and Maxwell, who had wanted to sell the stock cheaply to a wholesaler. My father never forgot that Ernie Pring stuck with them."

As a result, the company had to make wholesale reductions in staffing levels with only the essential technical staff retained. After Maxwell and Manners sold their interest in the company, both Verrells and Eric mortgaged their houses to provide some much needed capital and cashed in some insurance policies to secure a bank overdraft which would be needed to see the company through the few difficult months until the new 1933 season. Like a phoenix rising from the ashes, the company emerged stronger than before, mainly because of the wise decision taken in 1928-9 to engage top line engineers who, under the guidance of Eric Cole directly, set about designing new sets to a much higher standard and quality, which allowed the company to move up-market.

AD65 moulding line   (C.Poole)

Cole also commissioned two outstanding designers, Serge Chermayev and Wells Coates to design new cabinets for the company. Both of these designers had good reputations as architects and designers in the modern 'Art Deco' movement. The designers got to work designing new stylish radio cabinets, taking advantage of moulding Bakelite into unusual and creative shapes and breaking away from the previous convention of trying to get the Bakelite cabinets to imitate wooden ones. The result of this was the launch in 1933 of the AC74 radio designed by Chermayev, and in 1934 he followed it with the more attractive AC64. It was also the year the AD65 Round Radio by Coates, which, with its Wells Coates designed cabinet, truly became a piece of 'Art Deco' furniture to grace any contemporary room. The AD65 was produced in both cream and black, which was against the general principles of the trade which shuddered at the idea of trying to sell a black object. But this innovative round radio set was to out-sell everything else on the market. These architect-designed sets put EKCO back on the map and led to a further expansion of manufacturing

Wells Coates' winning design (DesignC20)

facilities. Now that the company was solvent again, phase two of the building plan could go ahead and building work began on a new office block and research laboratories, also designed by Wells Coates, facing the tree- lined Priory Crescent, in front of the existing factory. By 1934, EKCO was at the forefront of the design and installation of car radios, which were at that time a new phenomenon and very technically challenging. Launched at Radiolympia that year, they caused a sensation as well as quite a few headaches, not the least of which was that the normal radio shops had no garage facilities and garages had no radio expertise.

So EKCO had to set up a chain of installer-dealers. These sets, while not popular with some car manufacturers (who saw them as an unnecessary technical nuisance), soon became an optional standard fit for Rolls Royce. It was a deal which gave the company not only access to the Rolls Royce dealers and clients but the recognition from the world's best car manufacturer. This in turn influenced more manufacturers to, albeit slowly, offer customers the option of EKCO car radios. The overseas market was expanding but not without hurdles. In 1935, to overcome import restrictions on the continent, EKCO set up a manufacturing and distribution site in Belgium. This was only a small-scale operation but was to provide the EKCO management with a much experience of running an overseas operation and working with foreign nationals. The Belgium manufacturing unit initially used components shipped over from Southend but gradually it began to use locally-sourced components, which materially boosted sales and profits. This manufacturing unit, however, was short lived due to an economic downturn in Belgium following the German occupation of the Rhineland in 1936, and it was shut down in 1937. The sales and service department in Brussels, however, continued up to the start of the war.

EKCO began experimenting with television in 1936 through a joint-venture with a British company called Scophony Ltd, and attempted to negotiate a non-exclusive license for the manufacture, sale and distribution of Scophony television sets. The first set to go on sale was the EKCO-Scophony model ES104. Scophony were the developers of the ingenious projection television system, and these mechanical large screen models would have been aimed more at clubs and other public premises rather than the home. A sales brochure from 1938, describes the Scophony ES104 model screen as: "24 inch wide and 20 inch deep, giving in close ups a larger-than-lifesize picture and in long shots a breadth of vision which enables every detail to be grasped with ease." The model costs 220 guineas, and included aerial equipment and installation, plus a two-year guarantee and free maintenance, with hire purchase terms also available. The picture was projected onto a flat screen which folded into the cabinet when not in use. Customers were reassured that: "The picture was produced by optical-mechanical means and no high voltages or Cathode-ray tubes are employed."

Sadly, although the Scophony system showed great promise, its development was halted by the war and not resumed afterwards. Television however was clearly the future and Eric was determined to be at the forefront of this new technology. New buildings at the rear of the site were erected in 1935-7 to serve as the television research laboratory, as well as the car radio research laboratory, a component store and the service department.

The year 1937 was significant for EKCO as it introduced its own conventional cathode ray tube-based home television model (TC101), which also featured a built-in radio. It sold for the princely sum of £84 (around £4,800 in today's money). Consumers also had the option to purchase the set without the radio - model TC102 - for £47.5/- (equivalent today to £2,700). Orders and sales of these sets were not large since television (as we know it today) only began broadcasting in late 1936 (in 405-lines in monochrome analogue – high definition in those times) and only in the London area.

EKCO also set up production of their own radio valves, much to the annoyance of the established valve manufacturers. It gave EKCO the freedom and leverage to negotiate much better prices and pushed it further up in the league of radio manufacturers. The unit was sold as the Mullards Radio Valve Company in 1939.

The focus switched to television and in 1938 it introduced a low cost simple, efficient add-on television unit for use with existing radio receivers for the reception of television programs, priced under twenty-five guineas.

The domestic appliance division was also formed following the adoption of a patent taken out by a Scottish engineer, George Burnside, who had designed for the builders of the RMS Queen Mary a new type of electric heater for use in cabins that met the stringent requirements of both the Board of Trade and the ship's architects. This system was called 'Thermovent', and was soon widely adopted by other ship builders, including Cunard. Following this success, Thermovent was launched into the UK housing market and was destined to remain in production for around thirty years, another EKCO best seller.

Derek Cole with a Thermovent heater which he still uses to this day. (D.Cole)

Area circled is location of large underground ARS – for use by people in main hall.

Entrance here

Area shown is location for underground shelter for use by office and R&D with various access points

Aerial view taken in 1946 of EKCO Southend Works and the known locations of the underground shelters. (C.Poole)

EKCO works 1945

(C.Poole)

Chapter 4

The War Years

The war was to have a significant impact on EKCO as almost all its production was switched to meet orders placed by the armed forces, mainly by the Ministry of Aircraft Production. Development work on airborne radar began in 1939, and EKCO, because of its outstanding reputation for quality and innovation, was requested by the Air Ministry to participate in the research and development of AI (Air Interception) and ASV (Anti Surface Vessel) radars in order to bring the equipment up to a production standard - and then to manufacture it. Radio sets were also modified to listen in to the enemy. Needless to say, this work was done under absolutely 'Top Secret' conditions, and on a strict 'need to know basis'.

The importance of EKCO for defence work led to an MI5 scrutiny of the top EKCO management. Plastics expert Willi Hahn and his wife, who always spent August back home in Germany, were under suspicion and MI5 insisted that they be informed at once if they returned.

Derek Cole:
"On instructions from MI5, my father invited him home to dinner and at the end of it said, 'I am sorry, Willi, but here is your ticket for the night boat. I have orders to see you sail from Harwich tonight.' I do wonder if today, they would detain him here. His contribution was as big as the giant presses he brought with him. My father had many business friends in Germany, especially at AEG where they were very anti-Nazi. This had important post-war consequences. Once his occasional impishness had an unusual result and led to what he claimed was the first shot against the Nazis.

"Just after one Christmas he was dining with German business friends when the Nazi Gauleiter walked in and joined them at the table. At the end of the meal my father offered round some cigars. By accident, he had left a Christmas exploding cigar in place and it duly went off in the Gauleiter's face.

"My parents always said that they were at first deceived by signs that Hitler was getting things moving again and only later realised the full horror of the Nazi regime which they were to do so much to defeat. Ken Godsill recalled work starting on a wireless for an Army Tank in 1937 and I remember discussing the new Radiolocation (later Radar) round the dining table before the war, but the immense war effort of the entire radio industry was obviously top secret and I knew nothing of it whatsoever."

With the threat of war having loomed since early 1939, and the knowledge that air power and bombing would play a dominant role based on the experience of Guernica during the Spanish Civil War, EKCO began a program of building shelters; a mixture of surface and underground shelters across the site at Priory Crescent. Some twenty-six shelters in total were built, providing shelter for the entire work force of around 3,000 people (and accommodation for 2,000 vital staff). The factory featured very clearly on Luftwaffe maps from August 1941.

Hurried excavations were carried out under the building facing the sports field (this would be the lamp factory during the war and later became known as Building 9) at the rear of the site, which were only erected in 1937-8. Walls were dropped while deep trenches were carved out for the laying of a bomb and gas-proof shelter, which was constructed using two metre (6ft 6in) inside diameter concrete pipes (akin to those used for storm drains or sewers) that were craned-into place in the trenches. This was the fastest method available, providing a high security shelter capable of withstanding anything but a direct hit, which would safeguard the radar and key design personnel, the engineering personnel and the senior managers and directors of the company.

Heavy custom-made blast and gas-proof steel doors closed off the shelter from the world above. It was divided into three sections (called galleries). At each entrance at the bottom of the stairs there was a cleansing station where people who had been contaminated with gas could have been treated and washed down prior to going into the shelter. Each gallery had two chemical toilet cubicles and a drinking water supply. At the north end there was a fully equipped first aid station.

A power room was sited just off the central gallery. It was equipped with a diesel engine driving both a dynamo and an air pump. The shelter had its own power distribution panel where the lighting power could be switched over to an emergency DC power supply from the diesel generator should there be a mains failure caused by enemy action.

The air pump supplied forced air throughout the entire shelter network via a series of outlet pipes. The air would have been maintained at a positive pressure so as to ensure that the airflow was always outward - thus stopping the ingress of gas. At the rear of the power room was a small tunnel extension leading to an escape hatch, which led up to the sports field adjacent to the factory. Since the shelter would have been fully 'locked down' when there was a raid ongoing, the people inside had no means of knowing when a raid was over and it was safe to venture out. Consequently, above each exit door there

was an illuminated status sign which would have had a red and green mica panel showing visually the status as well as a bell system all of which would have been operated from above ground.

The tunnels were only revealed when the EKCO site was demolished in 2008. After a survey by the Field Archaeology Unit

Author Chris Poole (right) with John Anderson, of Ecomold in EKCO tunnel. (P. Brown)

of Essex County Council, all the fixtures and fittings from the tunnels (except the doors, which were too heavy) were removed and put into storage with the view to displaying many of them in a section within the new museum in Southend to give future generations an experience of what it was like to be in a Second World War shelter during a raid. There is no longer any access to the shelters on the Prittlebrook site.

In 1939 they became a way of life for employees. The air raid alerts were well rehearsed and everybody throughout the whole of the EKCO complex knew where they had to go once the siren was sounded. At the first sounding, appointed personnel (usually the juniors) would race down to the shelters and open the escape hatches in order to get fresh air flowing through the tunnels.

There was also a rota of fire-watching, the time spent on this being comprised of overtime and weekend work. The firewatcher's hut was situated on the roof of the main office block, and apart from sounding off the air raid alarms, the primary duty of the firewatchers was to keep an eye open for incendiary bombs falling on the site. From their elevated position they could direct the home guard and firemen to the location so that these could be dealt with before they took hold. However, in 1944 when the V2 rocket campaign against Britain started, there was a real problem since the first anyone knew of such an attack was to hear the detonation – and there were a few around Southend – and only then would the sirens go off.

Following the outbreak of war on 3rd September 1939, all work on domestic radios and televisions stopped. A plan had been laid out by the government that radio production would be stopped in Southend and moved to Aylesbury, Buckinghamshire, moving all the ancillary departments, including the machine shop with all its heavy equipment, the tool room and its machinery, and the maintenance departments to the new site. Production at the Priory Crescent site was switched over to 'war work', which for EKCO meant manufacturing the WS19, a mobile radio transceiver designed for the British Army to give armoured troops reliable communications which provided HF inter-tank and tank-to-HQ radiotelephone, CW and MCW communications, VHF inter-tank communications, and an intercom facility for a tank's crew. The HF 'A' setting was tuned to receive and transmit with a single dial and featured a 'flick' switch for rapidly changing between two frequencies, a device still used in aircraft today. The 'Bakelite' presses were turned over for munitions work (plastic practice bombs being one such item), and the lamp division was returned to valve manufacture.

Ella Chadwick:

"I remember that the domestic products were cleared out and production of 'tank radios' began. By this time I was a line supervisor, and one of my roles was making sure that the right girls were put in the work which suited them best. I always made sure that the girls with the steadiest hands were picked to put the valves into the sockets or for soldering, etc. My abiding memory of this work was the tremendous rush. At the end of May 1940, the order was given to evacuate Southend both at EKCO and in the town generally. I went to stay with my relatives in Purton, just outside of Swindon, where I received a telegram from EKCO telling me to report 'forthwith' to Cowbridge House, Malmesbury where I was needed.

"When I reported, things were fairly disorganised and there were a lot of girls who had been recruited that didn't know what to do, having not yet been trained. The other ladies and I who had been transferred from Southend then set about training these girls up and it was not long before we got production up and running. My role was to keep the line moving whatever, which meant that whenever a girl did not turn up for work I had to make sure another girl was available to take her place. I also had to make sure that the girls had all the components they needed, and sort out any problems they had. My immediate boss was a Mr Essex, which is a name I obviously remember being from Essex myself.

"At that time we had no idea what we were assembling, to us it was just another box of electronic components but what we did know was that there was a great urgency to get these made. Later on, we started to get 'directed labour' girls supplied to the factory, which caused some discontentment at times from the regular girls, and as the production hours ran from 8am - 6pm, it was necessary just to get on with the job because of the urgency and the demand for what we were making. Before long we started working 12-hour shifts, Monday to Friday, and quite often also worked Saturday mornings. There was also a fully-staffed 12-hour night shift that started after our shift finished.

"One of the good things about working for EKCO at Cowbridge was the fact that being formally a country house, it had a well-appointed kitchen garden, which was maintained and expanded during the war. The produce of the garden was a great asset to the canteen and so we ate well.

"I managed to find 'digs' in Oxford Street, Malmesbury, with my friend Helen Hemms, although there were lovely views over the valley towards Cowbridge, socially there was not a lot to do in Malmesbury, although there were dances laid on in the canteen every Thursday, and there was usually a dance somewhere in the town on a Saturday night. I left the company 1944 when I was pregnant with my son, and much to my surprise, the workers and the staff had a collection for me. I was presented with a nice canteen of cutlery with an inscribed plaque, and in addition I received £25 as a 'thank you gift' from E K Cole, which was quite a bit of money in those days. As I reach my 100th birthday, I look back with fondness of my time with EKCO."
(Ella Chadwick, 2008.)

In 1940, at the time of the Dunkirk evacuation, the threat of invasion seemed imminent, and the order was given by the Ministry of Aircraft Production to disperse manufacture away from Southend, which was considered to be in the front line. EKCO played a key role in the war providing the latest radar technology. What has only recently been revealed is EKCO's link to the Enigma monitoring by British intelligence officers.

Derek Cole:
"The EKCO works at Southend were a target for the Luftwaffe, and in Dunkirk week my father was ordered by the Ministry of Aircraft Production, which had just been taken over by Lord Beaverbrook, to move all war production to inland sites forthwith. Lamps and, under the guise of lamps, radar valves continued to be produced at Southend.

"A note of high comedy illuminates the history of this vital move. Malmesbury was already working, but much more capacity was needed. The ministry gave my father a list of available empty properties and he set out on a tour. Every ministry was doing the same and one of the first sites he enquired at had already been taken over by the Army. The nation was in a great panic remembering General Franco's claim that he had a fifth column inside Madrid. My father's enquiries raised suspicion and he was promptly arrested as a spy! A whole day set aside to arrange the move was lost until the village policeman eventually released him.

"This episode led the government to issue him with a high level pass. This he produced when, driving through the Buckinghamshire countryside on the night of the invasions scare in September 1940 with my mother, aunt and uncle, they came to a line of cars pulled onto the verge. A policeman demanded identity cards, but on sight of his pass he stepped back, saluted, and said, 'You may proceed, sir! But I should warn you we think German paratroops are landing'.

"He never said so himself, but my aunt's account was that on arrival home at Great Missenden he got out the rifle and shotgun for which he held licences. My uncle, who was called up and trained in 1918 but never reached the front, took the rifle to the back of the house where the field of fire was best. My father went to a front window and both their wives stood by as loaders. They stood on watch all night, but as we know it was a false alarm."

Mr and Mrs Cole c1945
(D. Cole)

ENIGMA

Radar work went to a secret factory hidden inside a country house (Cowbridge House) just outside Malmesbury. The head office went to the Green Park Hotel, Aston Clinton, Aylesbury, which was also used as a dormitory for office workers, who were required to fire watch on the roof two nights a week, and where Eric insisted on doing his turn. Radio production was split between the factories at Aylesbury and Woking, Surrey, and in all cases, the key workers were relocated as well. A site was also opened in Rutherglen, Lanarkshire, for component manufacture especially transformers.

"The colossal task of moving an entire major factory was accompanied in one gigantic effort. During Whitsun 1940, the ministry diverted a vast fleet of lorries to Southend and for hours the police closed the A40 to Aylesbury, the London North Circular road and all four lanes of the A127 Southend arterial road. This had been built in the 1930s, initially a single road, as public works during the Great Depression, a pale copy of Hitler's autobahns and Roosevelt's Tennessee Valley Authority.

"Opportunely, as I can well remember, the second carriageway reached the entrance to Southend at Kent Elms Corner by Easter 1939. In addition to the removal of factory and office equipment, personnel were also shifted, which in some ways was more difficult. People were uprooted from their homes with wives and children and billeted with the local population, which caused considerable suffering for all concerned. My father drove up the A13 to join the convoy at Gallows Corner and move to the new head office at Aston Clinton. He recalled vividly the extraordinary sight of an endless line of lorries pouring relentlessly up all four lanes of the new road.

"From his office at Aston Clinton, Eric directed important sections of the war effort in various parts of the country, and it has only recently come to light that he worked with Commander Ellingworth, who headed the team monitoring the Enigma transmissions throughout the war. This started in Southend, amending EKCO shortwave receivers as the first monitors of the German Enigma Code transmissions. The matter was so top secret that I suspect my father was chosen because he was the only head of company who could do it without telling anybody else. The report I saw from RN Medway is that Mr E.K.Cole did the work not EKCO. His work monitoring the Enigma code was astonishing news which only reached me in 2008!

"I recall my father saying that in 1939 that he had listened to Hurricane pilots shooting down a German reconnaissance plane. This may not have been mere casual interest, but checking on how effective monitoring might be. Throughout the war I listened to short wave stations all over the world on a top of the range EKCO set without having the slightest idea it was the basis for of a vital piece of war equipment. As the Luftwaffe reconnaissance photographs now in my possession show, the EKCO Works at Southend were an obvious target. Lamp production, not a high priority for the Luftwaffe, remained in Southend and so did Colin Godsill. It has only recently emerged that under the cover of lamp production the acquired valve know-how was put to use in the radar valve unit."

By 1941, AI mark IV and ASV Mark II radars were being made at Malmesbury, which was managed by Michael Lipman, while at Aylesbury, work started on the TR-1154/1155 transmitter/ receiver set, which was to become the standard set for Bomber Command for the duration of the war. Over 8,000 people were estimated to be working for the company across the various sites in 1944, when the company was the target of a "failed coup" as Derek Cole refers to the incident.

"Mark Frankland, who wrote a book about the founder of Pye, entitled 'Radio Man: The Remarkable Rise and Fall of C O Stanley,' referred to 'a scene known to any student of politics', the coup when the chief is away. The attempted EKCO coup against my father in his absence differed from the Pye coup, which unseated Stanley, in that he was not abroad, but he was totally incapacitated in the summer of 1941 by a nervous breakdown as a result of gross overwork since Dunkirk. Stanley of Pye also worked seven long days a week plus fire watching. Both men were different from other leaders of industry, including the wireless industry, who deserted their country in its hour of danger.

"What happened in the 'failed EKCO coup' is a mystery. All that is known is that the ministry considered taking over EKCO. I was only told that a director, who then disappeared from the EKCO story, plotted to dismiss my father and seize control of the company himself. The sudden disappearance of my father from his desk and his enormous responsibilities was a significant catastrophe, and the sight of the leaderless EKCO directors engaged in office politics as Hitler overran Russia must have caused great alarm. All the papers relating to this crisis were kept by my father in a suitcase at home, but bizarrely, this was stolen, along with lots of valuables from his home in Marlow in around 1960. The suitcase and the papers inside were found abandoned in a field near Heathrow. The burglars were caught and convicted, and my mother told me that my father had burnt the papers after I had suggested he should write his memoires."

It certainly did not impact on production. 'Centrimetric' AI Mark VII and Mark VIII radars were being manufactured at Malmesbury in 1942, and a year later, production return to Southend with the vast assembly hall manufacturing 'wiring looms' for bombers – principally the Avro four-engined Lancaster. It was also the year that EKCO's Woking factory developed the WS46 man pack portable 'walkie-talkie' set especially for the commandos. EKCO was also briefly at the forefront in lighting developments and lamp development. Later, 51 percent of the subsidiary company EKCO-Ensign Electric Ltd was sold to Thorn Electrical Industries, but it contributed well to company profits.

"Stanley, who had made the major electronic contribution to the war effort by developing the proximity fuse, turned his efforts away from wartime production to make illegal television transmissions so that he could beat the competition by introducing the first hugely improved post-war television sets. Meanwhile, my father was engaged in vital plans to modernise post war production for the benefit not only of EKCO but of the British people as a whole, having been sent by Stafford Cripps (the Labour politician who served in the wartime coalition government) on a trade mission to the USA to plan post-war reconstruction in the last three months of 1944. He sailed out on the RMS Queen Elizabeth as one of two

Eric Cole (left) with Jules Thorn (later Sir Jules) of Ferguson on their second trade mission to the USA in April 1946

Directors of EKCO meet the Sir Richard Stafford Cripps (centre) President of the Board of Trade, c1945

Jerry Bruinker, Chief Engineer (far left) Eric Cole and Tony Martin Technical Director (right) meeting a US General at Cedar Rapids, Iowa, USA, c1952

(All images D.Cole)

dozen passengers. The big liners sailed unescorted at great speed, flinging on 90 degree changes of course every few minutes. My father was in New York's Time Square the day Roosevelt won his fourth term. He returned with 16,000 GI's, many sleeping on deck, in December. Each group of twelve civilians shared four bunk cabins, allocated eight hours each. The only relief was coming up the Mersey, when the captain invited him onto the bridge to see the radar working. 'Do you know what that is?' he asked me. This was top secret, but we had discussed the principle pre-war when I was eight. I asked him, 'Do you mean Radiolocation?' and he replied, 'We haven't used that term for years'. In fact Radiolocation was dropped for RDF as the word location gave too big a clue to enemy ears. Fortunately, I was not in touch with Herman Goering. It became known as 'Radar' after the attack by the Japanese on Pearl Harbor.

"It was part of the war effort to pick up hitch-hikers. One day, heading for Southend round the empty North Circular, my father picked up a chatty gentleman and told him that he was going to EKCO. This drew forth the comment, 'Ah, that man Cole made millions', followed by a rambling, romantic and inaccurate version of the EKCO story. As he got out, his hitch-hiker asked, 'I never asked your name,' which brought forth the reply, 'I am that fellow Cole you were talking about, but there weren't any millions'. Almost as soon as the war ended, people started to claim they had served with my father in Iraq. It seems there was a Sergeant Eric Cole who was a signaler and he passed himself off as Eric Cole of EKCO. These stories kept coming in for about twenty years afterwards!"

The EKCO Home Guard

During the war, like at all the other EKCO factories, a home guard detachment was formed at Southend when Winston Churchill made the call to arms. Initially these volunteers were known as the LDV (Local Defence Volunteers). Given the size of the EKCO complex, it required a large number of men to defend it, and these were the 1st Battalion Essex Home Guard, 'B' Coy No 9 (EKCO) Platoon, which had its operational headquarters in an office within the main office building. They were commanded by Lieutenant (later Major) George R Busby, with 2nd Lieutenant HW Thornycroft as his second in command, and were supported by Platoon Sergeant EW Shepard, Sergeant Tim Dixon and Quarter Master of Stores, Sergeant Fred Coe. The platoon consisted of around 150 men (see Appendix 1) and was split up into four sections, namely the HQ section, the Vickers Machine Gun section, the Spigot

Mortar (bombard) section, and an 'other ranks' General Duties section. The HQ section had four sub-sections, namely the Watch, Stores, Clerical Staff, and Supernumeraries. The main duty of the EKCO Platoon was patrolling and guarding the main works, which was doing 'military' work and this meant that cordoning off the perimeter of the whole site (including the playing field). Rolled coils of barbed wire fencing were erected and the entrance and exit gates of the site were guarded, and everybody had to show their issued identity/works pass.

In addition to ensuring the safety of the works, the EKCO detachment also liaised with other Home Guard units in Southend and went out on patrol around the town. One known EKCO patrol line was along Southend seafront between the pier head and the 'Shore House' pub. This patrol line was split into four small areas so that each section had only a small distance to cover. Each patrol section consisted of six men and one non-commissioned officer (NCO), and while on patrol the men had to wear their steel helmets, have their respirators at the 'alert', have their 'gas capes' in position. Rifles were also carried with bayonets fixed and each man had five rounds of ammunition. The patrol lines operated at night between 9pm and 5am. Interestingly, the prime duty of the patrol was to watch for enemy landings on the foreshore (looking seaward) to see that no-one was damaging the defences, and to investigate anyone acting in a manner thought to be suspicious. The Vickers Machine Gun section had a prime role in assisting in the defence of the airfield by manning an anti-aircraft post close to 'Warners Bridge', which is adjacent

The EKCO Southend factory in 1941, protected by fences and guards. (C.Poole)

to the airfield, and an observation post was built in the middle of the roundabout, and a concrete block 'choke point' in Priory Crescent leading to and from the roundabout. Cuckoo Corner is a nearby junction of four roads, and was the strategic line of defence of the roads in and out of Southend. The approaches were defended by Spigot Mortars and the Vickers Machine Guns that gave a wide arc of fire.

Among their normal duties, the EKCO platoon also assisted the Police and Civil Defence in rescue, attending numerous incidents in the vicinity of the EKCO works including Thornford Gardens and Sherbourne Gardens (both adjacent to the rear of the works), where high explosive bombs damaged property with fatalities - notably No 29 Thornford Gardens, which was destroyed by a high explosive bomb on 9 July 1943.

In 1944, men from the EKCO platoon assisted when an American Air Force Liberator bomber crash landed short of the airfield when returning from a mission. It had just cleared the last house in Sherbourne Gardens before hitting waste ground, with wreckage ending up on Warner's Bridge, causing the closure of the road to and from Rochford for several days. One lady living nearby remembered going over to investigate and found a couple of chocolate bars, which she consumed with relish since chocolate was hard to come by at that time.

In a classic case of fiction mirroring fact, the EKCO platoon had quite a few 'Dad's Army' moments. One story relates to Lieutenant Busby (later Major) who at that time had a rather battered Austin 12 saloon which had seen better days. He suggested that this car could be used by the Home Guard and therefore arranged that the car had its original body taken off in the company carpentry shop and rebuilt from the chassis upward to resemble an armoured car although all the camouflage painted panel work was in ⅜" plywood since there was a shortage of steel plate. The top speed was probably no more than 15 mph and if steel had been used it probably would have been quicker to walk. The platoon received instructions in making 'Molotov cocktail' petrol bombs and one member of the HG remembers throwing these against the wall of the 'lamps building' for practice completely oblivious of the fact that there could have been people working inside! Whenever the weather was good on a Sunday morning, a favourite route march would be to the Rose Inn in Wakering (about five miles away) where 'refreshments' would be enjoyed before the march home. Like all Home Guard units nationwide, the EKCO Home Guard was stood down in December 1944, their job done.

In 1945, Verrells decided that on both health and age grounds he could not carry the company through the post-war years and resigned. As a stop-gap measure, Sir George Allen (an eminent solicitor of the day who had been

Edward VIII's solicitor at the time of his abdication, and was the first man to be knighted by our present Queen) became chairman of peacetime production, which was re-commenced at Southend. Aylesbury, Woking and Rutherglen were closed down, but Malmesbury was retained for military work. Domestic production initially concentrated on 'pre-war' designed radio sets until new designs could be developed.

Derek Cole:

"I was well aware at the age of fourteen that running a business was not to my father's taste, and my mother later told me that it was George Allen who had, with difficulty, persuaded him to take proper control and become the chairman himself. George Allen, the 'G' in 'Egen', (Eric, George, Ernie and Norman) the factory on Canvey Island, was replaced on the board in December 1946 by Derek Pritchard, who became commercial director. Pritchard headed the Victoria Wine Company, but all they could do at the time was allocate limited supplies to pleading customers, and he ran EKCO sales until his own company could start running a proper business. He later became Lord Pritchard, Chairman of the British Export Council.

"Towards the end of the war, with pre-war wirelesses wearing out and more households becoming out of touch, the Southend factory was allowed first to finish off the sets abandoned part-made in 1940 and then to make a cheap unbranded utility set.

"My father was a great one for table talk and the endless theme at wartime meals was the simple message, 'When this is all over, we need a United States of Europe.' His dealings with AEG had led him to visit Germany, a country he liked, and visited very frequently in the 1930s. German businessmen would say to him, 'This madman Hitler will lead us into war and we don't want it any more than you do.' This passion for European Union was to dominate his wider thinking for the rest of his life."

Chapter 5

Post War

While most companies in the post-war period simply picked up from where they had left off, EKCO was embarking on a whole new direction thanks to its integral involvement in the war effort. In 1946, premises were acquired on Canvey Island, Essex, and a subsidiary company, Egen Electric Ltd, was formed to manufacture radio components. Television production recommenced, and the Malmesbury division began work on nucleonic equipment (nucleonics is a branch of physics that studies the internal structure of atomic nuclei and nucleons, especially the exploitation of nuclear power). It also produced Cloud and Collision Warning Radar (CCWR). Another change was that Eric Cole had assumed the roles of Chairman and Managing Director by the end of the year.

Derek Cole:

"Stafford Cripps sent my father with Jules Thorn (of Ferguson) on a trade mission to America in 1946. They went by the newly available civilian air traffic. Heathrow was not ready yet and we had to drive him to Hurn (Southampton) Airport to fly via Shannon in Ireland and Gander in Newfoundland. Television broadcasts didn't restart until June, and we listened to the first post-war cup final, Derby v Charlton, on the car radio. Jules Thorn talked vigorously of his friendship with George Alison, the Arsenal manager. Under pressure from Roosevelt and Truman, American businessmen had been very helpful on both trade missions. Even while the war was still in progress, Roosevelt recognised the supreme importance for the stability of Europe and the security of the USA required the establishment of efficient modern industries in post-war Europe, starting with Britain. The trade missions my father went on were a follow up to lease-lend and a precursor to the Marshall Plan. The president of Ford Motor Company provided him with a detailed account and demonstration of their methods of production at 'Willow Run', Detroit, which in 1944 was full of B-17 Flying Fortresses.

"The main features of the production were the rolled conveyor units (mocked in Chaplin's film 'Modern Times'). On each section five women (always women in those days) did a specific amount of soldering to each chassis, which was then examined by a sixth person, the charge hand. It was accepted doctrine that no charge hand could control more than five people. The completed chassis then passed onto further conveyors through various test and inspection procedures. Although the works director controlled the work that was done, the chief of test answered only to the engineers and ultimately to Tony Martin, technical director for the technical quality standards required.

"If the buyers came to him to say that they could not get item 'A', which was on the stock list, for some weeks, but could buy item 'B' instead at once, Martin would quickly adjudge that either one in 100,000 would go wrong, and we could live with that, or alternatively that the failure rate would be unacceptable, so it should be vetoed. He had a flexible mind backed by acute judgement. Touring the labs, he would come across a development difficulty, suggest something the engineers hadn't thought of and move on. Frequently, this worked. He was quite a small man, and Jerry Brunker, chief engineer, summed it up in a basic principle: 'The little bugger's always right."

Martin led a team which kept EKCO to the forefront in technical improvements which the rest of the industry adopted. Automatic Gain Control, for instance, meant that the television picture no longer faded in and out if a plane flew overhead, nor did it shrink if the variable electricity supply of the time suffered a fall in voltage. In particular, his team developed one innovation that took competitors by surprise – the EKCO spot wobble - which oscillated the travelling spot slightly so that the lines were much less obvious. In 1947, an associate company, Kelly & Shiel (EKCO Products) Ltd, was formed in the Republic of Ireland for the assembly and marketing of EKCO products.

The plastics department at Southend was enlarged to incorporate injection-moulding plant. At Malmesbury, EKCO became involved with Fairey Aviation's development of what was to become Britain's first 'Air-to-Air' guided missile. This missile was primarily designed to counter the threat posed by enemy bomber aircraft, although it was also hoped that it could be used against enemy fighter aircraft. The missile program - code-named 'Blue Sky' - consisted of a supersonic dart powered by two booster rockets, which were jettisoned once the missile was up to speed, and was classified 'Top Secret' for obvious reasons. When the program reached the trials stage, the missile was called 'Fireflash'. Some 250 rounds were produced and a special intensive trials unit was formed at RAF Valley in Anglesey, Wales.

The Fairey Fireflash Missile   (Mark Busby)

At the time of development, air-launched anti-aircraft missile technology was in its infancy. None of the homing mechanisms used in modern missile systems had yet been designed, and so by using radar 'lock-on' technology, which was developed during the war, the missile was designed to ride a beam, whereby the host fighter would lock a very narrow radar beam onto the aircraft to be attacked. After its launch, the missile would centre itself onto the beam and fly along the beam until it reached the target. The system was developed in parallel with the infrared seeking 'Firestreak' missile (code-named 'Blue Jay') by the de Havilland Aircraft Company.

The ground launches were conducted at Larkhill, Wiltshire, but all airborne firings were carried out from specially adapted Meteor fighters based at RAF Valley. A similar program was being carried out using the RAF range at Woomera in Australia. The aircraft converted to accept the missile were the Gloster Meteor T Mk 7 (WA738 and WF781); Gloster Meteor NF11's (WD734/744/745 and WM374) at Valley, and WM372 & 373 at Woomera. A Hawker Hunter F NK4 (XF310), and Supermarine Swift F Mk 7s (XF115-XF124) used by No. 1 Guided Weapons Development Squadron at RAF Valley.

At the beginning of 1948, the production and marketing of EKCO lamps was taken over by a newly formed subsidiary company, EKCO-Ensign Electric Ltd, while at Malmesbury, Thermotube production began.

Derek Cole:

"Wells Coates designed two post-war major innovations, the 'Radiotime' (1947) and the 'Princess Portable' (1948). The first achieved the then technically difficult task of enabling the user to pre-set the time the radio switched on and off. The second used the wartime miniature valves and much smaller batteries to produce a set you could carry around. By 1945, the accumulator had disappeared but portable radios at first still used substantial high and low tension batteries.

"With the new Princess in 1948, it was a sensation not only on the beach in Holland (where we were staying on holiday at the time) but it also caused much amusement at school, where I proudly carried it on to the cricket field, only to hear the Australians run up a world-record 721 in one day in Southend against my native Essex.

In 1949, the Hadleigh (Essex) plant started radio production. This year also saw the association with the National Radio & Engineering Company of Bombay, India (a subsidiary of the vast TATA organisation). It resulted in the formation of National EKCO Radio & Engineering Company Ltd and a twenty-year agreement for the development and production in India of radio receivers, components and electronic devices, selling the products under the trade mark 'NELCO'. At Malmesbury, the Army WS88 set went into production for the British Army. This was a hermetically sealed unit that enabled inter-platoon radio at VHF. (This continued to be used by the regular army until the early 1970s, albeit in a limited capacity, and was still on issue to training cadets until the 1980s). The fighting was over in Europe, but a new kind of war based on differing ideologies was dividing the continent again.

"As the Cold War developed in the late 1940s, there were three Communist agitators within the company. Although probably not a security threat through lack of access, they clearly wanted to cause industrial disruption. One was arrested and jailed for paedophilia. Then there were two. One resigned when he won an important post at Marconi in Chelmsford. MI5 refused him security clearance and EKCO refused to allow him to withdraw his resignation. Then there was one.

"The personnel manager noticed that this last one was absent more and more, so went to his home on Canvey Island to investigate. He was running a cafe for holiday makers and making large profits. As my father commented, you can either be a hard-line advocate of 'The Dictatorship of the Proletariat' or a successful 'Capitalist Plutocrat', but not both at once. His absenteeism caused his departure to general amusement.

"My father fully supported Stafford Cripps' concept of Joint Production Councils, but regarded as absurd proposals to introduce a compromised sort of quasi-socialism in the form of co-ownership by shareholders and workers - halfway between nationalisation and the John Lewis Partnership model. However, he balanced the dividend with a Christmas bonus for employees. It was said that shop stewards were among the collectors for Sir Frank Salisbury's 1951 portrait which my sister now has, with a copy still in the EKCO Social and Sports Club.

"The small EKCO wartime activity in Rutherglen, South Lanarkshire, which was a severe black-spot in the Depression, had an interesting, and in the end, sad aftermath. To rescue these areas, Stafford Cripps at the Board of Trade introduced Industrial Development Certificates to control where new developments could take place, mainly because for fifteen years there was a great shortage of bricks. One day, my father's personal assistant came in and said, 'The president of the Board of Trade is on the phone.' When he picked up the phone, a voice said, 'Eric? Stafford here. This new radio factory of yours. Will you put it in Rutherglen?' My father replied, 'Of course I will.' The move got considerable publicity and the mayor dug up a carton of sand to put in the foundations. Some thought mud would have been more representative of Southend.

"Alas, these good intentions came to nought. The future lay with television, not radio, and the factory did not prosper. In his first budget, in 1948, Cripps announced that to simplify the tax system he was abolishing the 50 percent Purchase Tax (now roughly VAT). Some items would go to 33 percent but others, including radio, would be taxed at 66 percent. Listening with us, my father said at once, 'That is the end of Rutherglen.'"

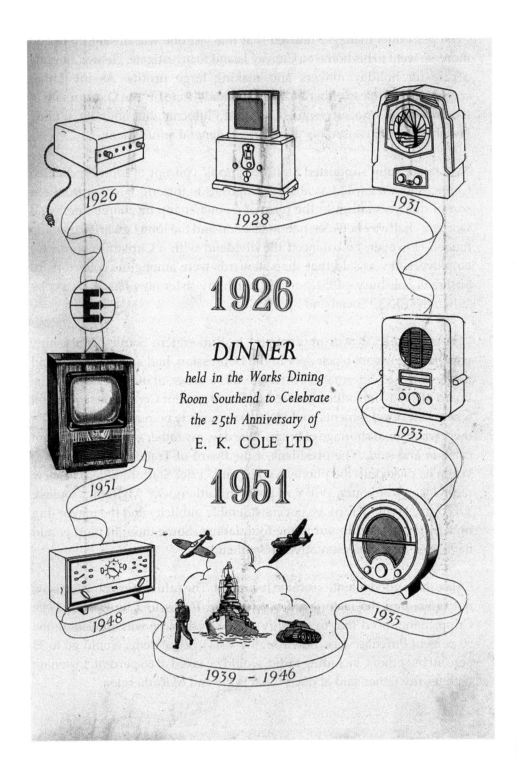

1926

1928

1931

1926

E

DINNER

held in the Works Dining
Room Southend to Celebrate
the 25th Anniversary of

E. K. COLE LTD

1951

1933

1951

1948

1935

1939 – 1946

(C. Poole)

Chapter 6

Expansion Was Key

Global expansion was key as the consumer boom of the 1950s got underway. EKCO was soon producing everything from pioneering defence radar equipment to baby baths, as well as leading the market in the latest TV and radio technology. Development work started on the successor to WS88 radio model (the WSA40) at Malmesbury in 1950, and at Southend, work commenced on a VHF radio system for Southend Waterworks Company. An associate company was formed in South Africa, Kruger-Wilson (Africa) Ltd in 1951, for the assembly and marketing of EKCO radio receivers. Its chief, Boris Wilson, was a South African MP and joint founder of the Anti-Apartheid Progressive Party. He donated a snooker table which was used in the EKCO club for many years.

Derek Cole:
"There was a small export department which always ran at a loss, in response to a major national export drive led by his friend Stafford Cripps, Chancellor of the Exchequer to earn foreign currency. This was more important back then, than the current British government's policy of 'Reducing the Deficit'. Year-on-year my father said in EKCO's annual report, 'In the national interest, these efforts must continue."

A new components production factory was built on Canvey Island, Essex, called Egen Electric, and at Southend, work started on the CE39 radio which was destined for use by the London Metropolitan Police. The following year, production of radiation meters started at Malmesbury, and work began on constructing a further Southend factory, located in Kenway, opposite the railway sidings at Prittlewell.

Production started at the new 17,000 square feet facility while construction was still in progress, and a permit was also granted for further building on the site to double the capacity should it have become necessary. The company's fast growth in the electronics field led to the formation in 1953 of a subsidiary, EKCO Electronics Ltd, to handle the marketing of EKCO ground and airborne radar, VHF radio, nucleonic equipment and other electronic devices. EKCO CE39 sets were used during the Canvey Island flood disaster and its Airport Radar Approach Aid (ARAA) was installed at Southend Airport. EKCO bought its first aircraft, an AVRO Anson (G-ALIH) in 1954, for the electronics team based in Malmesbury to use as a flying test bed to support their development work on weather radar. Of course, having a company aircraft also had a certain prestige in that it made a statement about how well the business was doing. Flight trials also commenced on Project 'Blue Sky' (fire controlled radar for the 'Fireflash' Missile).

EKCO also modified four De Havilland DH.89 'Dragon Rapides' to fly illuminated billboards to advertise "EKCOVision." The problem with it was that as these aircrafts went over the rooftops, everybody's television picture was disrupted with interference. Needless to say, It was a short-lived advertising scheme.

North America opened up to the company when the American Tradair Corporation of New York became a subsidiary company for the marketing of EKCO products in the USA.

The EKCO Dragon (Nick Skinner)

Derek Cole:
"The Montreal scheme was also successfully concluded, but Jerry Brunker, the export manager, became alarmed when the quote was being prepared because an engineer, whose wife was the secretary of an EKCO director, was moving to Thorn. Directors were advised verbally to divide by two the figure which appeared in the circulated costings. EKCO beat Thorn for the contract, and shortly afterwards Jules Thorn said cheerfully to my father, 'You fooled us on that one!'

"On Coronation night, Mr and Mrs Patrick from Montreal joined us for dinner and they were ecstatic that Canadian Television had beaten the US networks in flying the Coronation film across the Atlantic so that the EKCO sets in Montreal were among the first in the world to receive the pictures.

"The Queen's Coronation and the introduction of ITV provided two great boosts to sales in the UK. However, the former provoked an abrupt severance of EKCO's long relationship with the Palace Hotel in Southend. The manager had verbally agreed in advance with my father that EKCO could book the hotel for overseas dealers for the 1953 Coronation, and invitations were issued on that basis. Overnight, the hotel's parent company announced that they had signed a bulk agreement with a major travel agent and so refused to honour the promise to my father, who summarily directed that no EKCO money was to be paid to the hotel for any service.

"EKCO achieved world-wide coverage in 1955, with the first portable television that could run off a battery, albeit a large car battery. Sets were sold in the USA and elsewhere. I drove round Sydney with one in action. It is even possible that Eden's judgment before Suez was further impaired because the Australian Prime Minister, Robert Menzies, in London for urgent talks, tended to turn up late at Downing Street because he had ordered his chauffeur to drive round Hyde Park so that he could watch the Ashes on his EKCO portable."

The EKCO TMB272 portable television model produced in 1956
(Paul Marshall: golden-agetv.co.uk)

The TMB272 portables were heavy but were favoured by the BBC in the late 1950s as outside broadcast monitors for TV presenters to check that the shot was fine.

The main Southend factory was extended in 1955 to provide an additional 30,000 square feet of floor space to cope with the increasing demand for EKCO television and radio receivers. At the same time, the plastics division, by now one of the largest organisations, producing industrial mouldings and plastics domestic ware, installed vacuum sheet forming presses. The E-120 weather radar system went into production at Malmesbury (primarily designed for the Bristol Britannia aircraft), and Germanium transistors (using isolated Germanium as the metal semi-conductor) were first tested. While most of the early pioneering work was being done at Malmesbury, E.B. Thompson based at Southend, was busy capitalising on the good relations forged between the Ministry of Supply at Harwell and the Telecommunications Research Establishment (TRE) at Malvern. In 1955, he won the contract to design and manufacture the control room instrumentation system for the Dounreay Fast Breeder Reactor, being built near Thurso, northern Scotland.

The award of this contract allowed EKCO to move into a whole new field of expertise and was swiftly followed by a contract to supply control room instrumentation for Denmark's first nuclear reactor in Risø. This work however created a chronic lack of space within the existing research and development laboratories, which had to be shared with the commercial teams (TV and radio, etc). Therefore in early 1956, yet more building work began a new four-storey development and engineering block behind the existing research & development building. A controlling interest was also acquired by EKCO in Dynatron Radio Ltd (the trade name used by H Hacker & Sons), of St Peter's Road, Maidenhead, which manufactured high-grade radio, radiograms, television and electronic equipment. Meanwhile, the assembly and marketing of EKCO radio in New Zealand was put into the hands of an associate company, Ultimate EKCO (NZ) Company Ltd, of Auckland.[1]

EKCO Plastics Ltd, a new, wholly-owned subsidiary company, was formed in 1956. This company was responsible for the extensive range of industrial mouldings and 'Gold Seal' domestic ware formerly handled by the plastics division.

"The company was quick to adopt injection moulding and the EKCO baby bath won an award from the Design Council. In the official film of the presentation, the Duke of Edinburgh can be seen pointing to the certificate as he says to my father, 'EKCO is a play on your name, isn't it?'"

[1] *Derek Cole visited Ultimate EKCO in 1956 and 56 years later was able to tell EKCO's leading toolmaker Mr Leonard Smith, who was then in his nineties, that a split-pin he had developed for EKCO had made a major improvement to Ultimate-EKCO's production line.*

(www.rewindmuseum.com)

EKCO introduced the world's first mains/battery portable television receiver. The disadvantage of being first is that items go out of date first and no post-war country adopted 405 lines. This was a Marconi-EMI system that operated on very high frequency, and was the first fully electronic television system to be used in regular broadcasting, and became the standard for all British TV broadcasts until the 1960s. However, EKCO briefly got drawn into 525-line 60 cycle (in America) and 625-line 50 cycle (in Europe) exports, as some cities decided to finance their first television transmitter by taking a monopoly of the sale of receivers. An Australian company, jointly owned with

Associated Electrical Industries Ltd, was formed to manufacture radio and television receivers (including the EKCO Gondola RM204). This turned out to be a short-lived venture, and at the same time an associate company was formed in Colombia, E K Cole (Colombia) Ltd, of Bogotá. At Malmesbury, an automatic machine control system, believed to be the world's first, was developed for the precision engineering market. EKCO Electronics Ltd made history in 1957 by providing a complete nucleonic instrumentation system for the Hi Flux Australian Reactor (HIFAR) at Lucas Heights, which was the first experimental reactor to be exported from the UK, and was based on the DIDO Reactor at Harwell.

On 3rd May 1957, the new four-storey development and engineering department building was opened at Southend with a grand opening ceremony. In this building, nuclear instrumentation was developed for atomic reactors at Harwell, at Dounreay and at RisÆ in Denmark. In the meantime, the increasing application of radioisotopes in medical and industrial fields resulted in a continual output of new instrument designs. This building remained in use by the nucleonic teams for the whole time it was under EKCO ownership. Another important milestone in the development of the domestic radio and television field took place in April 1957, when the company launched Ferranti Radio and Television Ltd from its head office in Old Street, London, as a wholly-owned subsidiary to market receivers under the Ferranti trademark.

The range of EKCO heating equipment had also steadily expanded over the years, and in 1958, was further extended by the addition of a range of domestic reflector fires and a complete, balanced heating system for almost every conceivable situation. The heating range was further supplemented by the addition of EKCO 'Warmglow' electric blankets. In December, 1957, the one-millionth television receiver left the EKCO factory. At that time television production was running in excess of 5,000 sets per week and it would prove to be the pinnacle of its output. The phenomenal success of the firm had not gone unnoticed in the City nor in British society.

Eric Cole's CBE medal (D.Cole)

Derek Cole:

"My father received a letter in 1958 from Buckingham Palace offering him a CBE (which he received at an investiture from the Queen in November). As the Macmillan government also offered a large number of awards to trade union leaders who were financing the Labour opposition, I am quite sure that his large contributions, out of his own money, to Southend East Conservatives had nothing to do with it.

Unconnected with this, he was, however, angry when the Conservatives asked if he could provide a directorship with generous fees to a Conservative MP. He did not regard that as a proper charge on shareholders. At about the same time, Stanley had also reportedly rejected a suggestion that he should donate to a Conservative fringe group in the hope of getting a knighthood.

"One day, an unexpected visitor surprised Mr Faithful, the firm's commissionaire, by asking if Mr Cole was available. Using his usual impeccable tact, Mr Faithful finally persuaded him that he couldn't see the chairman without an appointment, so the visitor turned to the door, saying as he went, 'Tell him his father called.' At the age of about eighty-five, my grandfather had walked three miles from Crowstone Road. He was swiftly shown in and my father showed him all the new models planned for the Radio Show and eventually offered to call a car. This was firmly refused and my father stood watching him stride out across Priory Park, thinking, 'I wish I could walk that fast.'"

During the same year, a completely new factory was built at Maidenhead, to house the expanding Dynatron organisation. The Egen factory on Canvey Island was extended and modernised to provide a 50 percent increase in floor space, while the Kenway factory at Prittlewell was extended to cover twice the previous floor area. At Malmesbury, development work had begun on a 'ground-breaking' transistorised Airborne Weather Radar system (E-190), which was the first such system and was only half the weight of previous systems. Meanwhile, the ARI 5919 - 'Red Steer' (the code name for the tail warning radar system for the Victor and Vulcan 'V' bombers, which was able to detect enemy fighters) went into front line service with the RAF.

The major exhibitions of 1958 saw EKCO products surge ahead in every field. The EKCO car radio was offered in most leading makes of cars and the 'Superbath' was selected from the range of EKCO 'Gold Seal' domestic ware for the 'Design of the Year' Award by the Council of Industrial Design. At Malmesbury, a new weather radar system known as E-160 was produced for the De Havilland Comet IV (although this also sold successfully as an upgrade to the previous E-120 system). Flight trials were also underway with 'tail warning radar' for the 'V' bomber fleet (the Vickers Valiant, Avro Vulcan, and the Handley-Page Victor).

The extension of the EKCO plastics injection moulding shop was completed in 1959, and included the largest injection press in Great Britain. It made history with the production for 'Frigidaire', one of the first moulded refrigerator liners. The 1959 Radio Show saw the introduction of the slimmest ever television, an Ekcovision Portable Model, which weighed only thirty-one pounds, could run off the mains or a 12-volt battery, and could receive all the channels – both of them. It was an alternative to the standard televisions of the time, which were the size of a chest of drawers. As the decade drew to a close, some changes were inevitable within the firm.

Derek Cole:

"Ernie Pring always conceded he had no business flare, but as a director he came in daily to countersign the cheques, being noted for scrutinising the documents with care. Eventually, in about 1960, it became obvious he would have to retire. With post-war high taxation, he needed his director's fees, but as a non-executive director he was not in the pension scheme. My father was in extreme doubt that it would be a proper charge on the shareholders to pay him an 'ex gratia' pension, but was eventually persuaded by George Allen's firm that in view of his past services it was entirely lawful." (See Appendix II)

Plans were made to re-locate and consolidate the electronics business sector (radar, telecommunications and nuclear) in a new Rochford factory, and between November and December 1959, radar manufacture at Malmesbury was re-located to Southend and Rochford, thus leaving Malmesbury to concentrate solely on the production of heating products. (See Appendix III).

By the early sixties, EKCO produced a plethora of products including mains and portable televisions, mains (and battery) portable radios, radiograms, tape recorders, car radios, electric heaters, 'Thermotube' and 'Thermovent' heaters (these were convection electric heaters with concealed elements releasing heat upwards through vents – essentially an electrically heated tube), electric blankets, plastic toilet seats, various plastic utensils, plastic bathroom fittings and 'Superbath' baby-baths.

The EKCO Southend factory had become one of the most modern in Europe and a leading Swedish television importer, who was buying from Germany, said it was the most advanced that he had seen. In 1960, its modern, tooled production line made its rival Pye's Lowestoft plant look antique.

Chapter 7

The EKCO Social and Sports Club

One of the founding principles of EKCO was the provision of a social and sports club where employees could meet after work or at weekends to socialise, as well as participate in sports both indoors and outdoors. Accordingly, when the Priory Crescent site at Southend was built in 1930-31, a sports field and changing rooms block was laid out alongside the factory. The EKCO Social and Sports Club (ESSC) was effectively given to the employees and was managed through a trust fund administered by an elected committee. Each employee starting work for the company was given the option to join the club, and for those who joined (and the vast majority did) a small deduction was made through their pay packet for their membership fee. It was an instant success, with EKCO staff competing in year-round sporting matches, including football, cricket, netball, darts, snooker and billiards, against rival teams from Chelmsford-based firms Marconi, Hoffman's, and Crompton Parkinson. Before long ESSC was also organising dances and hosting huge parties at Christmas time for the employees' children.

The club also formed its own band, the 'EKCO Players', led by Richard 'Spen' Spencer, who in his day job worked as a life tester on the factory's completed output prior to mass-production. A competent musician, he led the EKCO orchestra for many years. Band practices were in the beginning held during weekend afternoons and weekday evenings at each other's homes. The EKCO Player's debut gig was a social held at the Studio in Leigh, where some fifty people attended. Once the canteen facilities were added to the factory, the band put on very popular canteen dances which would run for a complete season.

All of this naturally entailed a lot of hard work, as not only did the band play during the evenings, but members cleared the floor of all the tables, swept up afterwards, and provided even an occasional spot prize or two. As more musically talented people joined up, the 'Ekcoettes' were formed specialising in cabaret and chorus numbers, as well as solo artists, with many ESSC performers also providing entertainment at dances and social evenings at Southend venues such as the Winter Gardens, the Kursaal Ballroom and the Palace Hotel.

A fire in the ESSC clubhouse in May 1932 curtailed band rehearsals and canteen dances. The dances were soon revived by the club committee at the Drill Hall, on the corner of East Street and Tickfield Avenue, until an 'unofficial hop' which was tried at the London Hotel in Southend's high street proved very successful. The ESSC band soon became a popular choice for dance events in venues across the town.

The club's football team was also noteworthy too. In 1932, one of its most prominent football players, Samuel Prince Blott, was acquired by Southend United. As an amateur, he had already figured in their London Combination matches on several occasions. In his first game at the Kursaal against Charlton Athletic, he showed 'fine form', scoring a goal for his side during the second half.

Football League Positions to 12th November, 1932

Division I

Team	P	W	D	L	F	A	PTS
Westcliff Amateurs	6	5	1	0	17	5	11
Leigh Ramblers	4	4	0	0	18	2	8
Kursaal Sports	5	4	0	1	25	10	8
EKCO Sports	2	2	0	0	6	2	4

Division II

Team	P	W	D	L	F	A	PTS
Sutton Sports	7	5	2	0	28	8	12
Kursaal Sports II	6	5	1	0	31	9	11
Southend Corinth	7	4	2	1	32	12	10
EKCO Sports II	7	4	2	1	20	14	10

When the Southend site was evacuated in 1940, the plastics division remained, as did the social and sports club, and it was not long before an ESSC branch was created at the sites in Malmesbury and Aylesbury. During wartime there was limited opportunity for outside entertainment for the staff, so all three clubs played an important role in helping with staff welfare; many employees worked 12-hour shifts, and at Malmesbury, there was a lot of conscripted labour from all over the country.

It was equally vital in the era of post-war rationing and austerity, when a 48-hour working week was the norm, for staff to have a venue for relaxation and sports to raise morale. Most mainstream sports were catered for and the club also organised various outings - all of which were very popular. In the summer of 1946, a comparatively new member of the club suggested to the committee that the members should run - just for the fun of it - a Works' Pantomime. That was the beginning of the EKCO Players. The committee supported the idea, and as a result, in January 1947, 'EKCO and the Beanstalk' was presented in the works canteen for two nights subsequently extended to a third night by popular demand, not least due to the efforts of Richard Spencer. The scenery, the costumes, and indeed everything else, was all the work of the players.

A few months later, this vigorous new thespian group staged the Summer Revue 'EKCO-on-Sea' which ran for three nights to full houses. In addition to their canteen original runs, the Players took their shows to local hospitals and institutions all over the Southend and district area, resulting in brisk demand for concert party dates. The club activities became so large and varied, a quarterly magazine, the 'EKCO Social and Sports Club News', was produced to keep its members informed of all the activities on the pitch, off the pitch and socially.

A production of 'Aladdin and his EKCO Lamp' was staged in January 1948, followed that summer by the Players' first straight play, a comedy-mystery in three acts, titled: 'Such Things Happen.' The third panto, 'CinderEKCO', was staged in January 1949, and scored perhaps the biggest success of all, followed a few months later with a heavy drama called 'Heaven and Charing Cross'. The players measured their success in the fun they got out of it, and their reputation arose from the unique teamwork, which characterised every show.

To coincide with the company's 25th anniversary celebrations in July 1951, Eric Cole, as a 'thank you' to his staff, opened the new ESSC Southend clubhouse. Located off Thornford Gardens, the building is still in use today and is home to the cricket team, the EKCO Monarchs and Trojans, and the EKCO Whitecaps Football Club.

ESSC changing rooms (P.Brown)

Above: Children's Christmas Party 1951.

Opposite in costume: Cyril Andrews & Jack Barlow at a Christmas Party 1964.

Below: The EKCO Club in 1976 with Cyril Andrews, George Middleton, Frank Butler and Wally.

(Authors
Collection)

A major annual event organised by the ESSC at both the Malmesbury and Southend factories was the Children's Christmas Party which was held in the staff canteen and open to all employees' children. The parties, which usually featured children's entertainers are still remembered by people of many generations. Gordon Andrews, whose father Cyril Andrews ran the resident band in the Southend clubhouse for over twenty years, recalled being at the Christmas parties in the canteen while his father entertained.

"The Christmas parties in the clubhouse were equally memorable both at Malmesbury and Southend, where there was the opportunity to 'let your hair down' and the perils of 'drink driving' was something in the future; not that many people had cars in those days. The parties were varied each year; one year it was a cowboys-wild west theme and another year it was a 'Pirates of the Caribbean', and so on. My dad dressed as Captain Kidd did not fool me, oh no, 'Yo-ho-ho'.

"Every child received a gift (one year I got a wind-up tin-plate tank) and we all got a bag of sweets and an orange each! It was truly brilliant - it

really was! We had sandwiches, bottles of 'pop' and jelly trifles! After a fun-filled afternoon, my dad and the band would pack-up their instruments and move to the clubhouse to provide the entertainment and music for dancing for the grown-ups that night. The Christmas tree in the clubhouse used to be very elaborately decorated, with the usual baubles, tinsel, trimmings, and often had Disney characters and such fairy-tale themes which were all hand-painted by the talented Barbara Pearmain, who had been the club secretary for years. Reg Earle used to run the club and I believe he died of a heart attack whilst driving his car."

Left: Presentation of trophies at the Middleton Hotel, Southend 1968-9. Joan Peters is on the left.

Right: Each member of the netball team was given a copy of this photo by the Sports & Social Club as a memento of our achievement in winning all three trophies in the Southend & district Netball League season 1967-8. Joan Peters is in the front row, second from the left.

Left: EKCO and Plessey football teams outside the EKCO clubhouse in the early 1950s. Barry Peters is seated in the front row, third from right.

Right: The EKCO football team, with Bill 'Cam' Camfield in the Victory Sports Ground around the mid-1950s. Barry Peters is again third from the right in the front row.

(credit all images: J. Peters)

Above: EKCO Athletics Club mid 1950s. Center of picture clasping hands is the Head of Personnel, Mr R.R Laird and next to him is George Hobroyd, athletics coach, beside whom is Christine Persichetti who was the star long jumper of Southend Athletics Club and represented Great Britain at the Summer Olympic Games in Rome in 1960. Joan Peters is in the first row standing on the left.   (J Peters)

Derek Cole above competing in the 1984 Half Marathon. "In my last ever race I ran one lap of the EKCO half Marathon in 1984 and commented 'Henry. You made your WAY far too long'. I had to drop out to present the prizes. I am not sure if they gave me 007 on purpose!"   (D. Cole)

A popular event in the 1950s and 60s, at both Southend and Malmesbury, was the Miss EKCO contest. This was a very popular contest and the winner usually took centre stage on EKCO carnival float. The ESSC played a major role in both

events and organised the decoration of the float, which was used first for the Southend Carnival in mid-August and then again two weeks later at the Malmesbury Carnival. Sports days were held at both the Southend and Malmesbury sites and involved all of the inter-departmental contests competing, with finals and other knock-out competitions, some of which involved the children of employees. Mr and Mrs Cole, who were great supporters of the club, took great pleasure whenever they could in presenting the awards for these annual events held in June or July.

Muriel Cole presenting the title to Miss EKCO 1957   (D.Cole)

Joan Peters, worked at EKCO 1951-1965

"After leaving school at fifteen, I started work at EKCO Plastics as an office girl under the benevolent guidance of Mr W A Skellern, who was a very kindly gentleman and a great help in a strange new environment. I would cycle from Westcliff, which was where I lived before I was married, to clock in at 8.30am. After learning to type and take shorthand, I gradually progressed to become secretary to the Chief Inspector, Mr S 'Bill' Day, who was a very colourful character. He was extremely well read and could quote from Shakespeare or Hardy, but could also swear like a trooper, having been brought up in the East End of London.

"This first job was definitely the most rewarding. A continual stream of people would come through the door from the hierarchy to foremen from the line. I was responsible for making sure every relevant piece of paper was filed and could be retrieved like producing a rabbit from a hat. In addition to the correspondence sent to our vast network of consumers, many inter-departmental memos had to be typed and transported to various departments.

"The plastics department was somewhat rambling and involved quite a bit of leg work at times. At the weekly production meeting I took the minutes. This usually lasted all morning and was quite arduous. It involved many pages of shorthand which then had to be typed on special duplicating paper, run off on the Roneo and circulated to all concerned. It was very messy and there was a deadline.

"I remember very fondly my relationships with both management and staff. In the course of any day you would come into contact with dozens of people both male and female. As my own experience and knowledge grew, it was always rewarding to secure the respect and acknowledgement that you were contributing to the smooth running of the office. I was truly upset when the sales director purloined me and I was transferred to his team, although it was a promotion and I had my own office, I always missed the hurly burly of my previous position and the down-to-earth approach of Bill Day.

"In the sales department, the atmosphere was rather different. Tongues were smoother and sometimes fudged the truth in order not to rock the boat too much. A great deal of work at this time was keeping track of the Industrial Reps, i.e., those that brought in orders for parts to be used with cars, refrigerators, cameras, MoD work, etc. Typing estimates for jobs tendered and if successful issuing a MWO (Master Works Order) for the job. As sales director, my boss, Frank Pullen, would probably not be in the office two or three days a week, and so I was heavily involved with the sales manager and sales office manager.

"I finished working at EKCO Plastics in 1965. My job there was always most interesting throughout my career. Many people did not appreciate that as well as the radio and TV side of the business, we made plastics for Rolls Royce, Kodak, the MoD, as well as many domestic items: bowls, buckets, toilet seats, and baby products, etc.

"My future husband Barry and I were always keen participants in the sports side of the company. As many will acknowledge, we had a first-rate sports ground. I joined the netball club and we were very successful in the early sixties, winning many trophies in the local league. Another sport we both enjoyed was table tennis, which both Barry and I played as part of the EKCO Table Tennis Club.

"Barry played both football and cricket for EKCO and to instil enthusiasm in me for the latter game I became scorer for the Sunday side. The highlights of the calendar were the fixtures against Pye (cricket) and Plessey (football and netball), two companies that were also big players in the manufacturing industries at the time. I remember Barbara Pearmain, secretary to Reg Earle, who was in charge of the Social and Sports Club. How we girls all wanted to emulate her 'Doris Day' glamour. We also had two Carnival Queens from the ranks of EKCO personnel, and to be chosen as the Queen in those days was a huge honour. It took place at the Odeon Cinema and she was usually crowned by a celebrity of the time. It was always packed."

Above- Joan and Barry Peters at a Saturday evening dance in 1950s. (J Peters)

Below- Christmas Party 1960: Norman Diver and Bob Salmon on the left; John Eve, Eric Fielder, Dan Brennan in the middle, and Bernard Hutchings and Jack Spratt (with big moustache) on the right.
(D.Smith)

The 1950s and 60s were perhaps the heyday of the club, and was very much the social heart of the company where there was a lot more emphasis on home-grown entertainment. Ironically the advent of increased television ownership and broadcasting, particularly with the arrival of colour TV, meant the popularity of such events declined. Events were still held but people did not seem to take the same interest in making costumes and dressing up.

Chapter 8

Taking To The Air

The airport at Southend has always been vital for the local economy and is currently under a major expansion with daily international flights to an increasingly number of destinations. The EKCO factory was a two minute drive from the runway and was intrinsically linked both with the airport and the birth of leisure air travel.

In partnership with Southend Municipal Airport, as it was then called, EKCO developed the world's first Airborne Weather Radar for commercial use, and its involvement in Airport Radar Approach Aid (ARAA) was an early example of industrial and commercial co-operation.

It began in November 1946, with the appointment of Squadron Leader Bernard F Collins as manager of Southend Municipal Airport, who was tasked with developing the airport into a potential international airport, despite having a very limited budget and being shortage of materials. He was aware how the use of Ground-Controlled Approach (GCA) radar during the Berlin Airlift had materially contributed to the success of the operation by allowing aircraft to operate in all but the worst conditions (particularly at the Gatow and Templelhof airfields in Berlin), and proved that 'talk-down radar' was an invaluable aid to airports.

Collins realised that this equipment would be needed at Southend if it was to offer 'all weather' capability. However, GCA radar was hugely expensive (estimated at around £50,000) and only the military and large civil international airports could afford it, and so he arranged a meeting with EKCO. Local folklore says that Eric Cole was at a luncheon with the Mayor of Southend and Bernard Collins, where the issue of GCA talk-down radar was discussed together with its high price.

It was suggested to Cole that he could produce something cheaper that would work just as well, to which he apparently replied, "I'm sure we can."

Cole tasked Tony Martin, the chief engineer at EKCO, to investigate the feasibility of designing a system which would provide a talk-down service at a fraction of the cost of the existing systems. Martin sat down with his team of engineers, led by Ted O'Flynn, a wartime radar engineer with the company who ran a 'special projects' laboratory above the car radio laboratory.

Pam O'Flynn (Ted's wife):

"Ted O'Flynn was one of the original team recruited in 1929 to cope with the expansion of the business and forthcoming move to the new factory being built in Priory Crescent Southend. He started as a junior laboratory assistant and progressed to become a junior engineer by 1936, working on domestic receiver design - a position he held until the war and the evacuation and relocation in 1940.

Ted O'Flynn and Mr Burtensaw receiving gold watches for their Long Serivce Awards from Eric Cole in January 1955. (P. O'Flynn)

"He was re-located to the Green Park Hotel, Aston Clinton, which was once a Rothschild Mansion set in the Buckinghamshire countryside. This became the company head office for the duration of the war where in addition to being the HQ, also undertook research and development by converting the stables (a substantial building in its own right) to become not only laboratories but also a fully equipped workshop as well as a drawing office. Ted was engaged in the development of Airborne Radar at Aston Clinton, which was supplementary to the work being done in the Western Development Unit (WDU) at Malmesbury. It was here also that the Naval Radar sets were developed. Ted became responsible for an aircraft fitting party, carrying out the installation of Airborne Radar equipment in Fleet Air Arm Fairey Swordfish and Albercore, and the Supermarine Walrus at the nearby RAF Halton. After the war, Ted returned to Southend, and between 1945 and 1950 he was engaged in the design of VHF Communications and Direction Finding Equipment, which in the 1950's became widely used on airfields both in the UK and overseas."

The Southend team's work was made much easier by the fact that work on the Hawker Hunter Radar Ranging (ARI-5820) system at the Malmesbury factory was in the advanced stages of development. It was an almost a perfect match in terms of radar performance. A series of meetings were held between Collins, Martin and O'Flynn, along with engineers John Price, Mike Foggarty and Bernard 'Johnny' Walker. They established that the parameters needed by the airport air traffic controllers were a radar able to positively acquire and identify an aircraft (i.e. scan the surrounding sky) at a minimum of ten miles and to accurately talk down the aircraft on a three degree glide-path to the obstacle clearance limit height of 250 feet (at half a mile from touch-down), at which point the runway lights should be visible (failing which, the aircraft was required to abort the landing and overshoot to either try again or divert to another airfield).

The finished design was a structure resembling a periscope in a submarine. The operator stood at a three foot square console attached to which was a five-inch diameter 'A' scope and an illuminated compass above, which together showed an illuminated series of lights, and told the approach controller if the aircraft was 'on track', or off to the left or right. He was able to follow the aircraft by literally rotating the entire radar-receiving unit by turning it on its axis.

The whole of this console was mounted on a pole-like structure fixed at one end to the floor via a bearing housing with the other end projecting through the control tower roof, above which was a small gearbox and the antenna dish. This pole also held the waveguide feed to the antenna and two 'Bowden' cables, which controlled the azimuth tilt of the antenna via (quite literally) two motorcycle twist grips. As if on a motorbike, the operator would turn these grips, which were attached to a modified motorcycle handlebar, to rotate the whole unit through 360 degrees (if necessary) so that all runways were covered. Also attached to the front of the control console was a fixed microphone linked to the tower radio (normally set to the approach frequency) and a wraparound curtain to keep out extraneous light or shadows falling onto the 'A' scope. Once the parameters were decided on, development proceeded rapidly, so that by June 1949 the first tests were taking place at the airport, using a Percival Proctor owned by the airport as the target aircraft.

Between the wars, the airfield was mostly used by light aircraft and flying club members. The runway was still grass, illuminated at night by the placing and igniting of numerous 'Gooseneck' (paraffin) lamps. North East Airlines (a subsidiary of British European Airways) began operating cargo flights using Douglas DC-3s, Avro Ansons, Vickers Vikings, Airspeed Ambassadors and Bristol Britannia 100s.

By June 1950, the radar tests were completed, resulting in the system gaining CAA (Civil Aviation Authority) approval and certification in December 1951. The fully operational system was demonstrated to the press in January 1952. The airports known to have installed ARAA include: Southend, Swansea, Leeds/Bradford, and Elstree.

In July 1952, Southend Airport offered a year's training course for RAFVR operators for a fee of £3,675, which ran from September 1952 to June 1953. Eric Cole and Tony Martin went to America in December 1952 at the invitation of the US Military which was interested in ARAA, and to their surprise found that 'Time' magazine had run an article on the system, which was hugely satisfying to them. Unfortunately no sale was forthcoming from this visit. In 1960, the EKCO film unit recorded a visit to Southend Airport of the Mayor of Coventry and a delegation to view the Airport equipment described above.

This lack of sales is not surprising as it has been described as 'the poor man's GCA' as it did not have the height finding and reporting of the mainstream systems. Nevertheless it was an interesting project for EKCO and proved to be a very long-lasting and reliable system (possibly because of its simplicity), remaining in use at Southend Airport until around 1982.

The system at Southend was renowned for its accuracy of the alignment which had to be routinely checked. In the later years of the checking at Southend Airport, it was not unknown to ask one of the local (friendly) helicopter pilots to hover directly above a certain phone box, which happened to be directly on the centre line of 06 runway about one mile distant.

EKCO Ansons

As part of EKCO's quest to be the best weather radar manufacturer, no amount of laboratory testing could fully simulate actual flying conditions, and so to fulfil this need in early 1954, Phil Stride, the managing director of the Malmesbury site, put forward a request to Jerry Brunker at Southend, seeking the board's agreement to purchase a 'flying test bed' aircraft.

The request was agreed and it was decided that the aircraft had to be large enough to carry a team of engineers and be capable of conversion to carry the airborne radar then under development (the principal system being the E120 weather radar at that time). It was also necessary that part of the role of this aircraft would also be weather chasing to map and establish safety criteria, so a rugged airframe was a pre-requisite and this meant a twin-engine aircraft.

An AVRO Anson (G-ALIH) up for sale by 'BKS Engineering' at Southend airport was evaluated for the tasks. The aircraft called 'India Hotel' been converted to a thirteen seat configuration by its previous owner, 'Starways'.

EKCO's flying test bed, the Avro Anson 'India Hotel' (G-ALIH) at Shoreham in 1959. (P.Brown)

It was subsequently purchased on 6th July 1954, with BKS undertaking the 'nose modification' requested by EKCO following the sale. An advert was placed in 'Flight' Magazine inviting applications for a company pilot. Flight Lieutenant John D Meredith (128554), a former Second World War bomber pilot, then working as a pilot for Silver City Airlines based in Lympne, took the job as he said flying the new testing equipment offered him more of a challenge. He immediately became immersed in an intensive program of test flying, not only evaluating the E-120 weather radar system, but also taking Phil Stride 'cloud chasing', where Stride used the weather radar to map and photograph cloud formations in order to better understand them and use these photos to illustrate the pilot handbooks. In addition to the test-flying program, the Anson quickly became a popular workhorse for the sales team; the result being that Meredith regularly flew all over the UK, Europe and Scandinavia, with EB Thompson and O'Flynn both being regular passengers, promoting weather radar, the CRDF (Cathode Ray Direction Finding) equipment, and nucleonics products.

The Anson featured in a BBC newsreel programme broadcast on 16 December 1954 about the experiments being made with airborne weather radar, featuring the Bristol Britannia aircraft (the 'whispering giant'), which was very topical at that time. One of the regular ports of call was to Filton aerodrome to visit the Bristol Aeroplane Company, where the first civil weather radar contract (E-120) was underway for the Bristol Britannia. Filton was also the build site of the British Concorde, which was also fitted with EKCO radar. India Hotel was finally retired from service in September 1967.

EKCO replaced it with an Anson (G-AGPG), which was a slightly younger aircraft of 1945 vintage. After being registered to EKCO in October 1967, this aircraft named 'Papa Gulf' underwent a similar 'nose job' conversion to the first aircraft but this time the nose diameter was made as large as possible to accommodate the 30-inch diameter scanner dish required for the E-390/564 weather radar, which was a very advanced system with the first set being delivered to the Concorde teams at both Toulouse and Filton.

It somehow seems ironical that the world first (and only) commercial SST (Supersonic Transport) was having some of its vital equipment test flown in a pre-WW2 designed aircraft which was never designed to be a particularly fast aircraft even by the standards of even those days. It has only recently come to light that Ansons were used by 'Taffy' Bowen as flying test beds in 1937 when he was developing airborne radar at Bawdsey - a fact that would not have been known to EKCO during their ownership of Ansons.

Additionally, she spent a lot of time ferrying EKCO Instruments engineers to both the missile ranges at Aberporth and Benbecula in aid of the MDI systems, and other engineers and sales staff to Sunderland (Coles Cranes) and Monceau Les Mines in France (PPM Cranes) in aid of the SLI (Crane Safe Load Indicator) systems. On 2nd January 1970, her registration was transferred to Pye Telecommunications and she then spent a lot of time ferrying Pye staff between Cambridge and Southend, where it was apparent that the company was being offered for sale. With the closure of EKCO in 1971, Papa-Gulf was de-certified by the ARB and her airworthiness certificate withdrawn on 13th February 1971. She ended her days with 1948 hours 23 minutes on her airframe.

After languishing on the apron outside aviation traders' hanger at Southend Airport, she was moved to a new Historic Aviation Museum, which had been built adjacent to the airport on 5th April 1972. Here she resided under the wing of a Blackburn Beverly, slowly but surely decaying away. Sadly, this museum ran into financial difficulties and all the aircraft were put up for auction in May 1983. 'Papa-Gulf' disappeared from sight at this time, but she was next seen in pieces at the Brenzett Aviation Museum in 1986 before being moved north to BAe at Chadderton to be used as a source of spares for rebuild of G-AHKX (the Shuttleworth collection AVRO Anson 19). Sometime in mid-1995, she was transferred to AVRO Woodford for restoration by the apprentice school. Luck was prove elusive once more as due to a change of direction taken by AVRO-BAe, this was not possible so in June 2000 she was on the move again and after a short period with the Manchester Museum of Science and Technology went to the HPT (Hooton Park Trust) in Ellesmere Port on the Wirrel in 2007 to be restored. She was finally scrapped; the cockpit being bought by a private collector in 2012.

Chapter 9

Experimentation & Innovation

Radar development and the secretive war work feature in many of the memories of former employees of EKCO, as well the freedoms they had to experiment and innovate. Not to mention the social life offered to employees resulting in quite a few marriages.

Rose Henstridge, (employed 1942-1970)

"I joined EKCO at Southend in 1942, although most of the factory had been evacuated to Aylesbury, Malmesbury and Aston Clinton. I was allocated to office work in the temporary Drawing Office. Mr Burtenshaw was in overall charge of the office, although he was based at Aston Clinton, and I also remember writing to Stan Lind and Ron Kemp (*I think*) at Malmesbury. As production had just restarted at Southend on the Type 19 wireless sets and wiring looms for Lancaster bombers, we had to keep asking Aston Clinton for drawings and eventually we were allocated six draftsmen and three 'tracers' who were 'arty' people conscripted in because of their watercolour painting skills (and not their knowledge of mechanical or electrical items - of which they knew very little). Because they had been told to faithfully trace what was on the original, I remember one incident, which caused quite a laugh, when a lady tracer faithfully traced the outline of a fly, which had been swotted on the original.

"Working in the Drawing Office came in very handy in 1944, because when I got married my bridesmaids' dresses were made from 'rejected tracings' that had been washed out, and these were covered with 'lace' – coupon-free from Petticoat Lane Market near Liverpool Street Station in London. I left the company in 1948 to start a family, with the intention of returning to work in the early 1950s, but in those days no part time workers were allowed in the offices so I went into the factory making televisions. I loved working there and found it far more interesting than writing letters and filing, etc. My skills at reading technical drawings helped together with a good memory so I soon went 'full time' and became a supervisor. I joined the entertainments committee of the EKCO Social & Sports Club and well remember the children's Christmas parties where there were mounds of sandwiches made with sliced bread, margarine and tins of raspberry jam, although there were also jelly trifles and fruit cakes.

"In the late 1950s, I got to know Ken Hendry who had started up the avionics section in the Research & Development Labs at Southend, and he would often stop by and proudly show off new the bits and pieces. I well remember him showing me a small box of transistors, which he told me would do away with valves ('glass bottles', he called them); he was so excited that they had been sent to him from Malmesbury.

"When the Rochford factory opened in 1960, my husband went to work there; they were doing both avionic and nucleonic work. To be nearer the site, we bought a bungalow in Rochford and shortly after this I again left work. After about a year, Ken Hendry heard that I was not working and asked me to work at Rochford as a supervisor, which I did and again I loved it. The work was so much superior to the television work I'd done previously.

"Towards the end of 1960, we heard that Malmesbury was relocating to Southend and Rochford. As we had just settled into our ways of doing things, we were not looking forward to this at all, but in the event all was well. After a couple of years my name was put forward to run a section in the R&D Laboratories at Southend working on 'first off's' and bits and pieces for the Engineering Labs. This was wonderful since it also allowed me to renew some old friendships with people I had previously known in the television Drawing Office.

"In the mid-1960s, I found myself working on the E-390 project under Eric Golding, which was the radar destined for the Concorde; here I was with six good operators and we made the systems for the first two Concordes. As part of this I remember going to a seminar at the Café Royal in London, which was held for all those involved with the Concorde project.

"Shortly after this, the effect of the Pye takeover became apparent, and brought with it many unwelcome changes. I was offered a job on the factory floor making televisions - needless to say I left. By the end of 1970 it was apparent that all radar manufacture was going to be relocated to Mullard

Equipment Limited (MEL), which was owned by Philips Electronics, in Crawley, West Sussex, and my second husband, Roy Henstridge, was offered a job there. This we accepted, so we moved to Crawley.

"Again Ken Hendry heard that I was there and persuaded MEL to offer me a job as a supervisor, which I of course took. With various re-organisations, radar work ended up moving to one of their associate companies in Scotland, so Roy and I moved there to teach radar assembly techniques. This wasn't too bad because we met some of our old engineer friends, as well as quite a few 'test' men, some of whom I'd worked with way back in my television days.

"I'm eighty years old this year and my local library gave a party to all the townsfolk who had reached that age. We all had to say something of what we did from the war onwards and when Concorde was mentioned, I told everyone about my contribution to the radar, which resulted in a lot of men telling me about their radar experiences in the war."
(Rose Henstridge, née Fisher, November 2006.)

Pete Terry, (employed 1961-1964)

I joined EKCO Electronics in 1961 as an indentured apprentice, starting in the television production lines, and I developed an interest in radar whilst working on secret airborne radar in the test department at Rochford. I was introduced to V J Cox, the chief engineer, through the agency of one of his staff with whom I shared a digs in Brightwell Avenue. There was a protocol for addressing Himself. Senior engineers and departmental managers were allowed to call him 'VJ'. Everyone else had to use 'Sir'. Apprentices were expected to treat him as God.

"The following people were already there, as far as I remember: Ray Moxon, John Churchill, Robin Wilcox, Colin Pike, Brian Linge, John Wallace, Ken Simms, Frank Burnhill, and Ron Lee (who always seemed to be shaking things and squirting hot brine at them for long periods). The 'Gaffer' was Jack Halsall, who lived in the adjoining office with Bill Graville and Ray Southgate.

"From my school days in the early 1950s I had an interest in electronics and learned that there was a colour code for wires: Red for Line (as now wrongly called Live); Black for Neutral; Green for Earth. When graduating to the use of valves, I discovered that actually Red was for High Tension positive, Black for Earth, and Green for Grid, all very confusing. When starting on a wiring job in 'Radar 1', I enquired whether there was any sort of regulation colour code. I was advised that there most certainly was. It stated that the colour of any particular wire was immaterial, but... it shall be the same colour at each end.

"Also lurking about was the resident laboratory assistant we nicknamed 'Yogi Bear', who was even more of a tearaway than I was. He had developed, to the level of an art form, skiving - the technique of discretely disappearing when anything half resembling work reared its ugly head; or else he went off sick with some improbable reason such as hard pad or distemper.

"A few other people I remember include Sid Parr in the winding shop. He was the only known person able to roll his own cigarettes using only two strands of 'baccy'. We developed a scale of calibre in 'Parr' units for roll-ups, based on his technique. Zero Parr was equal to the empty fag paper, and one Parr was equivalent to a Player's Navy Cut. Few of the others who rolled their own could get much below fifty Parr.

"There was a chap called Armstrong in the Standards Lab downstairs. He and his department moved to somewhere round the back of the Research & Development (R&D) block, and his old lab became the Inverter Lab. Yogi was permanently assigned to him, shortly after which Armstrong went off permanently sick! I spent much of my time testing scanners in the radar shack on the roof. The shed was built with one side made of Perspex, presumably to be transparent to 10GHz, which is not far off infrared, so the atmosphere in the shed was like that of a greenhouse in summer.

The Electric Fence

"A major project I remember developing was the Electric Fence. 'VJ' was going camping and his wife apparently didn't like the cattle to approach the tent too closely, so the EHT experts in Radar 1 were directed to build an electric fencer unit as Priority One. The output power and PRF (Pulse Repetition Frequency) was to be similar to that of the new radar being developed for Concorde. The device was duly built and was found to be many times more powerful than the best commercial unit. Should a cow have chanced to touch the wire with its snout and got away without frying, it would probably have jumped clean over the moon.

Secret Drawings

"Nearly all of the drawings in Radar 1 were restricted or classified. One came up from the Drawing Office which had been stamped in big red letters TOP SECRET along the top margin above the standard notice directing DO NOT SCALE. It was not long before some wag had scribed along the opposite margin BOTTOM NOT SO.

Security

"'Old Harry', as he was affectionately known, was the security officer. He had been issued with an impressive uniform, a comfortable armchair and a desk on a bit of carpet in the foyer. His function was to greet any visiting dignitaries and to lock up at night. One day, a new engineer joined the lab, and whilst still green, he pinned-up some drawings on the wall behind his desk. The trouble he got into for doing this was nothing compared with what he got next. All drawings were considered to be secret, whether marked so or not, and were not to be displayed on walls where they could be viewed through the windows by spies with binoculars in helicopters. When finished with drawings had to be replaced in the filing cabinet. Our green engineer was told to get rid of them, so he tore them down and deposited the shreds in the waste-paper bin. This resulted in a very stern rebuke indeed from the management. All obsolete or damaged drawings must be taken down to Old Harry for proper disposal. When asked how he disposed of old drawings, Harry replied, 'I tears 'em up and chucks 'em in the waste-paper bin.'

"It seemed to me that practical joking was a main occupation of everyone in the department. I was told that this discipline had been imported along with those transferring from Malmesbury some years before. I particularly remember the case of the 'Little Gem Fuse Blower' where a nice little box the size of a half-brick was obtained and sprayed with radar black crackle paint. The engraving shop supplied a regulation label marked Little Gem Fuse Blower, followed by a suitable military part number. A mains cable came out of a grommet at one end and was terminated with a plug, which fitted the sockets around each bench. Inside the unit the three wires of the cable were soldered together and the lid screws 'araldited' in to prevent removal. The device was placed in a strategic position on one of the benches by the door. By their very nature, engineers are an inquisitive species and tend to interfere with anything that does not require fixing before it's broke. Hence, no one was able to resist this device. The usual procedure was:

1. Inspect device
1.1 Pick it up
1.2 Read label
1.3 Mutter, "Wonder what this does?"
2. Plug it in
2.1 Discover what it does
2.2 Pull out plug and carefully replace device as if untouched
2.4 Furtively slink back out through door
2.5 Avoid eye contact with the crowd falling about behind the glass partition
3. Get stepladder and roll of fuse wire to repair the power supply to the room.

De-Smoking

"There was an extra-high tension generator in a nearby lab, and with a pair of electrodes fashioned from paper clips a nice fat satisfying spark could be generated. One engineer had been trying unsuccessfully to give up smoking for some time. 'Radar 1' was always up for a challenge, and this looked like a good one. Whilst out of the lab, his desk drawer was raided and fag-papers removed. The packet was carefully opened up and the papers passed through the said fat spark. The packet was re-assembled and returned to the drawer. The spark had no visible effect on the papers but had micro-perforated them. The engineer eventually lurched back into to the lab gagging for a roll-up, and immediately made one. It was most entertaining watching him huffing and dragging on the thing without getting any sort of a draw at all. He never did rumble what had gone wrong, but guessed his colleagues, who were all looking the other way and whistling tuneless tunes, had something to do with it.

The day we set fire to the roof

"The subject of spontaneous combustion arose one day, with the regulation disbelief and heated arguments. At EKCO Radar the usual manner of settling any such arguments and disputes was to set up a suitable experiment. In this case it was the belief that acetylene would catch fire and possibly explode when in contact with copper, which would act as a catalyst. I was using a carbide head-lamp on my bicycle. This was more efficient than the electric lights available before high-power light-emitting diodes were invented half a century later. I demonstrated that because the lamp was made of brass, it had to be heavily chromium plated to keep the acetylene away from the copper content of the brass.

"The experiment was to drop some carbide into the fire bucket whilst Yogi, who had been issued with a lump of copper and a big hand file, was told to get cracking. There was still a small quantity of water left in the bottom of the bucket and some carbide was thrown in. The mixture heaved and crackled, bubbling up in an alarming manner and emitting foul-smelling grey fumes. When Yogi's copper powder was chucked in, the effluvium rapidly became overpowering, so the contents of the bucket were heaved out of the window, landing on the flat roof above Gibby's lab. The reaction continued but no combustion. However, someone solved this with the agency of a match. This produced a minor explosion and an impressive conflagration which kept the lab entertained for some time.

"I repaired to one of Yogi's several funk-holes to compile a suitable excuse, should one be required. Strangely, no-one else witnessed this event except the group in the Nucleonics Lab which faced ours. Apparently they weren't much impressed and took no notice. They held the Radar Labs in utter contempt, their engineers being a lower form of life prone to indulging in stupid and irresponsible experiments. This view was, of course, totally erroneous.

The Magnetiser

"The magnetiser was a fearsome beast, lurking in the Standards Lab between Gibby's Mechanical Lab and the Drawing Office on the ground floor. It crouched on a low bench, waiting, like the Hound of the Baskervilles, to spring at the throat of anyone foolish enough to chance his luck in switching the thing on. There was a crank and lead-screw mechanism for raising and lowering the top pole-piece. Several hand-wheels were arranged around the top. From one dangled a notice warning the operator to ensure that these were limbed up pretty tightly before switching on. A large wad of Tufnol held the poles safely apart when not in use.

"I was fortunate in never having need to use the thing, but I did see it in operation the once. On this occasion someone was attempting to re-magnetise his bicycle dynamo (properly called a 'Magneto', this is a type of alternating current generator in which the magnets rotate, leaving the windings stationary). The dead magnet had been stripped out and, because of its odd shape, had been clamped at an equally odd and unstable angle between the poles of the magnetiser. Although the hand-wheels were done up with the aid of a length of pipe, it was clearly not good enough. Upon switch-on, the machine emitted a mighty hum which would have done justice to Battersea Power Station. This built up to a level sufficient to rattle the clamping system loose, as I took refuge under the bench in the opposite corner. The whole system's chattering and vibrating rose to a crescendo like a demented rock drill. The draughtsmen next door were drawing wiggly lines, and twenty-five television sets, soak-testing in the lab two blocks away, dropped out of sync. I half-expected Ron Lee to come bursting in with a prototype gear-box, demanding to test it on the new vibrator. The furious magnetiser was eventually pacified by switching off with the aid of a pair of lazy-tongs borrowed from the Nucleonics Lab.

"It was a traditional belief that the machine's magnetic field was so powerful that a hand placed in it would be instantly reduced to a soggy dollop of amorphous protoplasm. Should anyone mention this in the lab, it was usually met with a round of guffaws.

"When these had subsided and tears had been wiped from engineer's eyes, the many protests indicated that this could not possibly happen as a DC magnetic field would have no effect on any part of one's anatomy. The Laughing Engineers, however, refused to set-up the regulation experiment to prove it. Odd that.

The Chip Fryer

"Sometimes referred to as the 'Coal Scuttle', the designers insisted that the new efficient cooling system would not let it get hot enough to fry chips. I did not have much to do with this equipment as I left EKCO Radar shortly after this event. However, I do remember the prototype demonstration to 'VJ'.

"The equipment was configured as a horizontal, back-projection system so that the navigator could use it as a plotting desk. The system comprised basically a two-foot square Fresnel lens as the desk-top screen, a high-power projection cathode-ray tube below, between the operator's knees, and a periscopic arrangement to focus the display on the screen. The vertical control panel was above and at the back, making the system look exactly like a chip fryer or coal scuttle. There had been much head scratching over the previous few months. The problem was that a suitable mirror had to be found for the periscope. It had to be of optical quality, light-weight, but had to stand the impact of the odd boot or two, not injuring the operator in any sensitive area should it chance to shatter. The problem was eventually solved by stretching a sheet of metallised polyester over a frame, like a silk-screen. There was, apparently, great difficulty in getting the stuff mounted wrinkle-free. After much effort a decent example was produced which satisfied all the requirements, and it was bolted in the display ready for inspection.

"He appeared most impressed, and in order to test the integrity of the system, he acquired a lit cigarette, (deemed not to be an unlikely accoutrement of the eventual radar officer), and proceeded to burn several holes in the polyester mirror. This was accompanied by the muffled groans of the several engineers who had repaired to the sanctuary of the dark corner by the coffee-brewing apparatus. This treatment did not appear to cause the projected image to deteriorate much, so I guess the system passed muster.

"I recently designed a huge 3MW generator for windmills. This machine required some big permanent magnets from China, from where all the neodymium comes. When I received a letter from China saying, in Pidgin English, that although they could easily manufacture the magnets, they would not be able to magnetise them because, '... there am no such machine big enuff', I thought of my days at EKCO radar.

"I was out of my indentures in 1964 and left the company, but many of the electronic and mechanical tweaks and dodges acquired during my time have served me well to this day, fifty years later. However, I am having increasing difficulty in finding anyone who speaks the same language. How many people nowadays know what a slide rule is, or a trochotron, or a klystron? What is a getter? They all think that a microwave is a machine for warming-up one's lunch, and not a packet of energy calculated to addle one's brain whilst radiating from the mobile telephone permanently clapped to the side of the head." (Pete Terry, January 2013)

Medical Counting Lab c1965:

Tony Wilde (standing, left), George Loveday and Bob Hubbard (standing right), (sitting L-R) Russy Narielwalla, Pat Saunders, and CJ Tirion (a visiting Philips engineer)   (B Hubbard)

Bob Hubbard, (EKCO Nucleonics 1957-1971)

"After an interview with nucleonics chief Engineer Peter Harvey and a visit to the Personnel Department, I was told I could start work in the Medical Counting Lab, and all that I (and anybody else) needed to work at EKCO was a card and a cup. The card was my National Insurance card and the cup, I found later, would be filled with EKCO tea twice a day by one of the famous canteen ladies. What more could a chap want? The Personnel Department had found me suitable digs in Beedell Avenue and I started work in the Medical Counting lab, located in the Development and Engineering building – the 'Dev and Eng', as it became known, in October 1957. I recall many characters.

The Dev and Eng building

Ground Floor	Model Shop	Run by Jack Bishop-Leggett along with Fred Ellis, a mechanical engineer.
First Floor	1) Coil-winding Dept - 2) Buying Dept - 3) Lab	1) led by Sid Parr, with J K White & John Grant 2) run by Cyril Walters 3) run by Eric Fielder

Second Floor	4) Three nucleonic development labs:
	    i) Industrial Lab
	    ii) Reactor Lab
	    iii) Medical Counting Lab
	
	5) Applications Lab
	
	6) Prototype Wiring and Assembly
	
	7) Nucleonics Store
		4) managed by W E Thompson
		    i) headed by Tim Davis
		    ii) led by Bob Davis
		    iii) led by Jim Streeter
		
		5) run by physicist Doug White with Ernie Hodgson & physicist, Alan Innes, with Geoff Jefferys.
		
		6) run by Joe Stephens assisted by Alan Layton, Alfie George, Lily Penn, Glenys Edwards and Betty Short.
		
		7) manned by Tom Turnidge, an ex-policeman, assisted by Peter Petitt

Third Floor	8) Drawing Office	Ernie Burtenshaw ran the larger Radio/TV section. Jack Knight ran the Nucleonic section with senior draughtsman Ken Mileson. Other draughtsmen included John Worsdale, Fred Palmer, and Paul Andrews.

"Alan Innes was easily recognised in the tea queue. His tea mug must have been capable of holding at least two pints! Mr Knipe had a small workshop on the second floor and made special mechanical parts for the development labs. He was a precision engineer and was reluctant to make anything from engineer's sketches that showed 'approximate' dimensions! I recall Peter Bliss and Joe Browne also did time in the Drawing Office, but I'm not sure when. John Worsdale was also a member of the Zenith Jazz Band, while Fred Palmer was renowned for his home made wine made from a packet of dried parsley! There were about six tracers in the Drawing Office, under the leadership of Mary Wallaker. These were girls who were particularly good at ink tracing (on a linen type material) over the pencilled drawings made by the draughtsmen, thus producing a hard wearing drawing 'master' suitable for printing. The Drawing Office Print Room was run by Helen Leach. Technical Publications department was also located on this floor.

"Ernie Murphy translated engineers' scribbled circuits into presentable diagrams for inclusion in service and instruction manuals. Technical writing of the manuals was done by Tony Harrison. The Technical Library was run by Mrs Tucker who circulated technical periodicals around the labs. If you spoke nicely to her, she would copy and bind selected articles for you. Mr Seymour provided the admin services for Dev and Eng and the Avionics dept. One invaluable service, seldom mentioned, was the costing of redundant materials, often made available for staff purchase. I can recall acquiring some moving coil meters for a few shillings (a few 5ps). They were probably scaled in millirads/hour (the unit of absorbed radiation dose) or something similar!

"Jim Streeter headed the Medical Counting Lab and was supported by a senior development engineer Pat Saunders, who was the brother of Eric Saunders in the Avionics Department. Pat was a good engineer, but in winter he would refuse to buy anti-freeze for his car. He would drain the radiator each night and refill it in the morning. At least, that was his story, and he stuck to it. I don't think anybody believed him! Russy Narielwalla and Terry Middleton were also members of the lab at this time. Russy later changed his surname to Nariel, I guess because people couldn't remember it, let alone spell it! I was initially put to work under the watchful eye of Pat, developing the N600 Linear Ratemeter and N610 Automatic Scaler for nucleonic work.

"The scaler provided continuously variable control and metering monitoring of either threshold or gate voltages with automatic or manual scan mode via a single switch. The N610 replaced the earlier N530 Scaler and employed trochotron beam switching tubes in the first two counting stages. These were thermionic valves having a 27-pin base and a glass envelope surrounded by a powerful cylindrical permanent magnet. By using trochotrons, a significant reduction in components was made, coupled with a counting speed improvement. But there was a drawback. If a trochotron was left on a bench, it would invariably roll towards any nearby lump of steel (the mains conduit at the rear of the bench was favourite) and attach itself. If left overnight the magnetic field became sufficiently distorted to render the tube unusable. So they needed a little 'TLC' and were best stored in their original boxes or plugged into their associated equipment.

"Robin Cornish, a graduate, also started on the same day as me, worked on the N616 Vibrating Reed Electrometer, an instrument for the measurement of very small currents (of the order of femtoamps) produced by Ionisation Chambers. George Loveday, a former apprentice, joined the lab at some point (possibly early 60's) and worked on a new medical diagnostic unit, the N668 Gamma Camera. The early versions of this unit contained valves and some germanium transistors but later models, I believe, were fully transistorised.

"The Gamma Camera was essentially 'a pin-hole camera made of lead'. Gamma rays, from a radioactive tracer in the subject, entered a large area thallium-activated sodium iodide crystal mounted inside a lead shield. Sodium iodide crystals used in the Gamma Camera and Scintillation Counters were all grown, tested and prepared in EKCO chemical labs. These were used to image gamma radiation emitting radioisotopes, a technique known as scintigraphy, the applications of which were used in early drug development to view and analyse images of the human body of ingested radio nuclides emitting gamma rays. Most equipment built in the labs was tested at some point with a radioactive test source.

"Ron Glover was the Nucleonic Radiation Safety Officer whose primary job was to keep tabs on all radioactive sources in the company, some of which were stored in the Applications Lab. He was also responsible for the Radiation Safety Badges issued to all lab staff. Occasionally, some prankster would leave his radiation badge in close proximity to a radioactive source (over the weekend for example), which resulted in looking as if the wearer had received an apparent massive overdose, indicated by the change in the colour of the film on the badge. Needless to say, the perpetrator would receive an earful from Ron.

"Norman Jerrum designed the mains transformers used in the power supplies of these units, which provided +300V and -105V (regulated) DC supplies. The transformer had numerous secondary windings and usually included a 450-0-450V winding. This was not very 'finger friendly' if you were a bit careless during testing.

"Louis Szymocha was in charge of the Test Department (he later changed his surname to Sheldon), and John Dowding was responsible for the manufacture of any special test jigs needed by the Production Test Department. George Oxley, brother of John Oxley in EKCO Plastics, ran the packing department, providing an essential service to all departments in Dev and Eng.

"The instruments described so far formed part of a large range of medical counting equipment being developed at this time using thermionic valves. In those early days, reliability of such equipment was often impaired by the poor performance of so called 'high stability' carbon film resistors. Resistor values above about 50k ohms had a tendency to drift high or even go open circuit. It was not until metal oxide resistors became available in around 1954 that this problem disappeared. Transistors and ultimately integrated circuits were yet to come and would make dramatic changes to the size and performance of this range of equipment.

"A new breed of IC-based instruments thus evolved, which employed one double-sided printed circuit board housing all components, mostly IC's. These were 'slim line' units weighing only a fifth of the weight of the earlier valve units. The first of these was the M5024B Scaler-Timer. This was followed by the M5183 Digital Ratemeter, which also employed, probably one of the first, EKCO Thick Film Circuits designed and produced by Joe Phelan of the chemical labs. This circuit contained a ladder network of matched resistors used in the digital-to-analogue circuit of the Ratemeter. Other (non-medical) nuclear instruments were developed in the Industrial lab. These included radiation monitors, thickness, fluid density, metal wall and moisture gauges. More recent units were the M3182 Mineral Analyser and M8524 Bore Hole Logger.

"Sadly, in the late 1960s the Nucleonic Group was bought out, with, I believe, some other nucleonic companies, by Nuclear Enterprises. The EKCO Electronics name was changed to EKCO Instruments in 1970, and I remained with the company, developing the Crane Safe Load Indicators until 1982."

Dave Smith, (employed 1957-1961)

Dave Smith with his wife Barbara (D.Smith)

"I worked at EKCO Southend from 1957-61 in the Research and Development Labs (the white curved cornered one opposite Priory Park) and have fond memories of the scanner hut on the top of our labs - I spent many happy hours in there as well as on the airfield at Southend with the old AVRO 'Annie' Anson that was our test bed. My department was headed by Peter Harvey but my immediate boss was Eric Fielder, a super guy who didn't exactly control us but sort of directed us, if that was possible.

"My colleagues (that I can recall and name) were: Norman Diver, Bernard Hutchins, Bernard 'Johnnie' Walker, Jack Spratt, Alan Acres, Clive Brown, Bob Salmon, Dan Brennan, Peter Bliss, and Ken Crispin. The mathematician was Max Callendar (of 'Callendar's Steam Tables' fame) who had a body thermostat problem and lived in his office in sweater and overcoat with the heating turned full on, all year round. Without doubt though, the most important person was the tea trolley girl, Hettie.

"As you entered our lab, mounted on the wall was a small wooden frame surrounding a pair of blue velvet curtains and gold tassels as seen on most commemorative plaques. These curtains were always closed, but if a visitor had the temerity to open them, they were confronted by a photograph of E K Cole framed in a plastic toilet seat (courtesy of the plastics division) under which was written *OUR FOUNDER*. We also had a most ornate electric kettle fitted with a pair of eagle's wings! Wonderful place to work, if a little eccentric!

"Before joining EKCO, I served my National Service time in the Royal Navy Air-Sea Rescue Helicopter Squadron at Lee-on-Solent and our VHF radios were TR-1934, TR-1935 and TR-1936, all four-channel crystal-controlled sets and TR-1520, a ten-channel covering the whole band. Upon joining EKCO I found myself in the laboratory that had designed those systems but there was nobody remaining from that team. Within weeks, a problem occurred with the RAF using these sets and my baptism of fire was to be sent to RAF Cranwell to sort it out.

"I arrived at the railway station together with a whole herd (I choose my words accurately) of new recruits. Outside the station was a fierce NCO who had a grudge against everybody and he proceeded to bellow at these new lads and herd them towards their transport, sort of cattle-trucks. As I didn't respond to his shouting he viewed me with suspicion and as he was obviously one short he marched purposefully towards me. At that moment a large RAF staff car swept into the station yard, pulled up beside me and the staff driver leapt out smartly to open the door and help me in. I looked back at this bewildered NCO who had stopped in mid stride and was contemplating just how close he had come to death! He had no idea who I was (indeed neither did I) but a staff car obviously made a huge impression on him. The RAF thought I was some whiz engineer from the designers and I was treated royally. Fortunately the problem turned out to be straightforward and I returned home to triumph, my new job at EKCO secured.

"I have never seen any of that equipment from that day on. It was affectionately known at the 'going-going-wheeee' machine on account of the noise it made when changing channels. It had a rotary transformer that doubled as motor to drive the crystal turret. The 'wheee' was the 1K tuning frequency heard for one second.

"The radar equipment being worked on at EKCO at that time was a manual GCA unit designed for small mobile airfields. It was mounted in a MONAB (a sort of four wheeled towable chicken shed) which resembled a tall filing cabinet mounted on a central spindle so that it could rotate 360 degrees, and was controlled from a pair of twist-grip handles mounted one each side, similar to a submarine periscope. The method of use consisted of the operator rotating the scanner round 360 degrees looking for a return 'blip' on the screen which, if located would be maximised by dish elevation control. Once the range and dish angle was identified, charts were consulted that would give altitude of the target.

"If a fixed radar location could be determined, mechanical linkages (cams) were placed on both elevation and direction and limit switches fitted. Of course, if the equipment was mounted right on the end of the runway, no cams were required but this was a very unhealthy place to be as the first successful talk down would cause the aircraft take the dish away with it as it landed! This equipment was delivered to us for the inclusion of a VHF direction finding and communication set so that the operator could talk directly with the aircraft. This set had a rotating Adcock aerial (about four revs per sec) and a second CRT was added above the 'A' presentation which was a PPI with suppressed brilliance (a bit like me really!) so that an aircraft calling on the approach frequency would appear as an illuminated line on the screen in the direction of the transmission. This could be switched from QTE to QDM and gave the operator the exact bearing for him to turn the radar for location and the precise direction for the aircraft to fly to the base.

"I took one of these to the 1960 Farnborough Air Show to demonstrate its abilities. Several days into the show we were visited by three senior American military personnel, one from the USAF, one from US Army Air force and one from US Navy and they were obviously not impressed by the simplicity and basic design of the kit and were loudly verbal about it (I think 'Mickey Mouse' was mentioned). Nevertheless, they asked me to show them how it worked. Each day at the show, a Coastal Command Shackleton took off from the airfield for a 24-hour patrol and this had become airborne about fifteen minutes earlier to great acclaim from the air show commentator.

Left: A coastal Command Shackleton was picked up twenty miles away by an EKCO radar identifier at the Farnborough Air Show in 1960. Right: EKCOs mobile GCA unit at the air show.

"It just so happened that I knew that the previous day's flight was always stacked about twenty miles downwind awaiting clearance to make its landing as soon as the current flight was airborne, so I did a slow sweep of the sector and sure enough, at twenty miles was a large 'blip'.

"I proceeded to show them how the 'blip' was maximised and how range and altitude was achieved but they were clearly not impressed. So I then explained that the character of the 'blip' told me a lot about the nature of the aircraft. This got their attention. I looked carefully and said, 'First of all this is a four-engined, propeller driven aircraft...' Now I had their complete attention. As the range of the aircraft closed I gave a clear description of the aircraft I had seen take off the day before and as it entered finals, they stepped outside to see the exact aircraft I had described land and taxi away.

"A very subdued trio came in again and looked in awe at this now state-of-the-art-radar identifier and took away all the info they could, after thanking me profusely and shaking me by the hand. I often wonder if they went away to describe this miracle radar that the 'Limeys' had to their appropriation departments. This GCA equipment was installed at Southend Airport and was in constant use up until the early 1980's when it was phased out with the introduction of ILS. It was, however, retained as a back-up and was certainly used into the early 1990s. It gave a very accurate talk-down but it did need an experienced operator."

Dave Smith and colleagues
celebrating Christmas at work

(D. Smith)

Chapter 10

An Apprentice's Story

EKCO was a main apprentice employer of Southend for over 30 years. Two apprentices share their vivid memories of their first jobs.

John Brown, (employed 1950-1955)

"On Monday, 16 October 1950, I caught the trolley bus from Chalkwell School to Priory Park gates, walked through the park and reported to the East Gate of the EKCO Works at 7.50am, as told to do so in my letter of engagement. There were many others in the waiting room - surely they were too old to be apprentices? Gradually the numbers reduced as I realised these were new 'works' employees. A youth, much about my age, asked for me and I was led through the offices to Mr Neale's office where he greeted me warmly. He was a very perceptive person and realised how I was feeling in a strange environment on my first morning.

"My first six weeks were spent in the auto shop, which was full of 'Ward' automatic turret-control lathes and older overhead belt-driven Ward lathes. The foreman was George Kirkby, a genial father figure; the charge hand I was put with was Ernie, a likeable northerner. I was first shown how to use a micro-meter and told to become proficient with it, since it was used extensively for checking the piece-parts manufactured by the lathes. Generally, I was made to feel very welcome, although as the apprenticeship scheme had only recently started, I was the first they had encountered. After a time working alongside the fitters, I was allowed to do some setting-up myself, and then have it checked out by the fitters.

"I made the inevitable mistakes of moving the long wooden arm, which moved the over-head belts onto another pulley wheel, too fast, resulting in the belt jumping off the intended pulley. A fitter then had to laboriously climb up a ladder and move the belt back on again. But apart from these occasional mistakes, I gained confidence and competence, and was allowed to do other jobs around the workshop, including the spinning manual presses. These were usually operated by female labour, who, though rough and often coarse, were cheerful souls.

"When I first started work in the clattering and noisy Auto Shop, with its mixture of smells, Paxoline (the generic name for synthetic resin bonded paper or cotton cloth), coolant fluids, oils, and so on, I used to come home after my nine hour day with a splitting headache, but I gradually got used to it. The day started at 8am and finished at 6 pm, with one hour for lunch. On Fridays (pay day), we were allowed out at 5pm and queued up by the clocking machine in the stores area, where we were called out one by one by the pay clerk to receive our pay packet. I was paid £2-10s-1d (less deductions) for a forty-four hour week. As for clocking on, there was no allowance for lateness; if up to three minutes late, we lost fifteen minutes pay, and more than this if half an hour late, and so on.

"One further memory of the Auto Shop, given today's stringent health & safety regulations, I remember with some amusement was the use of steaming baths of carbon tetrachloride that were used for de-greasing and were also very effective for dry cleaning our overalls and brown dust-coats. We must have inhaled gallons of the stuff! When it was time to move workshops (after six weeks), I was quite sorry to leave as I had become accepted by more or less everyone, and made some good friends. My next role was in the Press Shop. This time it was work on a far larger scale, complete television and radio chassis, and it was heavy work at that. The press tools were massive and often needed three people to transfer a tool from a trolley to the machine. Everyone was on piecework and the attitude was quite different. To have an apprentice placed with an operator usually meant their piecework rate would be adversely affected. My situation was not helped by my apprentice predecessor who had gained a reputation for being idle and disinterested - so it was assumed that all apprentices were the same. After a spell, I was moved to a different part of the Press Shop and was lucky to click with one of the setters. Thereafter, I had no problems, and they were sorry (or so they said anyway!) when it was time to move on.

"This time it was the stores, and I was taken to meet Mr Juniper, the Superintendent, and Charlie Pead, the Foreman. I was allocated to Cables and Small Components (resistors, capacitors, laminations - for transformers), and supervised by another Ernie (who was elderly but very helpful) and his assistant, Reg.

"One day, I was allocated a place on a working party to Rochford Aerodrome to move and load dozens of EKCO Thermovent heating units stored in some ex-RAF seco huts. These were prefabricated structure of cellular hollow plywood 'aero' beams and columns clad with timber framed units of flat asbestos facing sheets and a felt roof. Designed as airfield accommodation, they could be re-used as post-Second World War emergency housing. On another occasion, my job was to take a trolley down to 'Goods Inwards' to load heavy boxes of transformer laminations. Having off-loaded them again into stores, an hour or so later, I had to load them back again on to the trolley and transport them to the Assembly Lines in the main factory, also known as the 'Willow Run' (after the famous factory in Michigan, USA).

"When I initially joined EKCO, it was decided that I would follow the Engineering Apprentices Training, which meant the National Certificate Course, undertaken at Southend Municipal College. I started with Year S1, (having been excused Pre-S1 because of my secondary education). The Engineering Department was under Mr Bernard Thomsett, a blunt and almost self-educated man who had been a Chatham Dockyard Apprentice; he was obviously very proud of his successful struggle to higher education, but who rather spoilt it by his over-long stories of self-glorification and name-dropping of his association with Clayton and Shelley, two electrical academics. Mr Thomsett was an ardent socialist and revealed this when he came in to the S1 class shortly after I had joined it. As I recall, he considered the class too large, and (I heard later) that the City & Guilds Craftsman's Course needed more students. In his blunt way, he demanded to know who had been at private schools; some hands were raised (including one of my fellow EKCO apprentices). 'Right, you're out then!' The number remaining seemed to satisfy him, and I breathed a sigh of relief; one time when a state funded education was an advantage. I think as most of us discover in our life this is usually the converse!

"The Engineering Department had just moved into splendid purpose-built and well-equipped premises. We were generally fortunate with a good lecturing team - my first year was Ken Varcoe (Electrical Engineering), Mike Drinkall (Mathematics), and Mr Jennings (Mechanics). The year 1951 was the 25th anniversary of the foundation of EKCO, which had grown from a small workshop producing radio battery eliminators (sold through bicycle shops) to a huge engineering combine manufacturing radios, car radios, televisions, plastics, electronics and avionics, film and radar equipment, nucleonics, and electrical components, as well as lighting and heating equipment.

"To mark the 25th anniversary, the company commissioned trains to take employees from all the UK factories to Harringay in north London for a special performance of 'Rose Marie on Ice'. You could take your spouse or a friend, and each guest was given a sandwich box and drinks. I asked Joy Field, a friend from the Municipal College days, and we enjoyed a wonderful evening; the show culminated in Mr and Mrs E K Cole being conveyed by husky-drawn sledge around the huge arena.

Silver Jubilee brochure (P.Brown)

"After a three-month spell in the Stores Department (which included a two-week stint in tool stores), I was told I would be joining the car radio assembly production line. Mr Entwhistle was the foreman and Miss Diana Coppin was the super-officious charge-hand. Initially, I was put alongside the various women operatives to learn each stage of production; some were connecting and soldering a few components, others were doing more complicated work such as the station tuning drive cord assembly. The work was timed so as to achieve a continual 'float'.

"After a short time I had learnt the various operations and found the work very monotonous; women were better at repetitive work and could chatter away at the same time as they were working. Sometimes to alleviate the monotony, I would mischievously purposely work extra fast, sending down an extra float of work which meant the operatives had to work harder - and they complained! Diana would then move me further down the line to deal with the extra work - served me right. One morning I nearly invoked a strike as I plugged my soldering iron in at 7.55am, instead of 8am - I was accused of starting work too early - irons took five minutes to warm up and I was setting a bad example. The factory was a noisy, hot and smelly place. I can still hear the air-driven screwdrivers being used, and the clatter from the overhead gantries where cathode ray tubes were loaded into hessian bags and conveyed down on a rail to be taken out by operatives on the television assembly lines.

"As Sutton Coldfield (the Midland TV transmitting station) had opened the year before, and Holme Moss, near Manchester, was to open in 1951, and the demand for television receivers was very high. Southend at that time was geared to producing five thousand units a week! Car radio production in comparison was far less: our two versions of the CR117 amounted to about five hundred Ford versions per week, and five hundred Standard models (sold through car show rooms). The Ford contract was important to the company - every Ford Consul and Zephyr was installed with a radio; a rather plusher version was introduced for the Zodiac when that entered production at Dagenham.

"One recollection from this time was an amusing tale of pilfering, told to me by fellow apprentice, Dick Jarrett, who was a colleague on the ONC (Ordinary National Certificate) course. One winter's evening, shortly before finishing time, one of the fitters got a colleague to help him to tie a large Record Bench Vice with cord from his neck, the weight being supported on the crossbar of his bicycle. He then hid it under his gas cape. When the 'finish work' signal pips sounded at 6pm, the fitter cycled out with the rest of the works personnel towards the east gate. It was an icy evening, and as the fitter neared the exit, he unwisely raised one hand as a greeting to one of the duty security men, and called out 'Goodnight'. At which point, the bicycle wobbled and slid on the slippery surface, dumping him on the roadway. The security man ran across to give assistance, but couldn't help noticing that the cyclist was having extreme difficulty raising himself up. He smelt a rat! When he tried to assist the person to his feet, he found him to be unusually heavy; further investigation revealed the Record Bench Vice. Needless to say the fitter was sacked.

"Just prior to the Christmas holiday, the EKCO Social and Sports Club organised two major evenings at the Kursaal Ballroom; one for the works' employees and the other for the office staff. The resident orchestra, led by Howard Baker, provided the music and the singers, and the EKCO management funded a super buffet on both evenings. It was a most popular event, and with the Kursaal Ballroom having the largest sprung floor in the southeast, you could really feel its movement on the final 'hokey-cokey' of the evening.

"On the day when the EKCO Works closed for the Christmas holiday, the factory was a dangerous place to be - especially for a seventeen year old - dominated by at least three thousand women on the assembly lines. Although alcohol was specifically forbidden from the premises, the workers would smuggle bottles in and hide them - sometimes under the floorboards - weeks beforehand. By 10am, the bottles would appear and the place got rowdier and rowdier. After the lunch break, when most poured (literally) into the local pubs, things rapidly deteriorated - until the works manager said, "Enough's enough," and sent everyone home. During the final jollifications, I recall one young man was stripped totally and sent down the production line! Any man was at risk anywhere on the site.

"I was fortunate in that I went to Development & Engineering only eight months after starting with EKCO; on the training plan it was normally the final year that one entered the Research Department.

"Thus, on 12 June 1951, Mr Neale took me over to Mr Maynard's laboratory. Mr Maynard was a large, rather severe looking man with a moustache and heavy glasses and clenched a pipe between his teeth. He had two former grammar school assistants, both in their early twenties, Colin Rance (ex-Westcliff High School) and Geoffrey Galpin (ex-Southend High School). I was regarded as the 'lab boy'. This was a television laboratory, which had just designed units for the new T161 triple-link chassis. The other television lab was run by Mr Norman Atkinson, (a more approachable person), and his two assistants were John Bussell and George Baerselman (a brilliant time-base engineer who was eventually poached by Ferguson's), plus a lab boy, John Baker, (about the same age as me). A tall bird-like figure with dark piercing eyes was M V Callendar (Max); a clever and brilliant academic who drifted in, held highly erudite conversations, and then drifted back to his own office again. Very union-minded and leftist, he was somewhat remote.

"My work was mainly measuring dozens of pre-production chokes, transformers, and coils in the Standards Room - on a complex Sullivan and Griffiths Bridge and various Wheatstone Bridges. The Standards Room was in the charge of a Mr Morgan - a delightful fatherly figure who was kind to all young apprentices (such as me) and always was on hand when we got out of our depth - which was fairly often! Occasionally, I had to go and use the test equipment in the Test Engineering Standards Room - again the staff were always helpful.

"One day, I had a bit of a drama. Colin Rance was working on a 15-inch CRT, which he noticed had gone 'soft' and he saw that a crack had appeared near the EHT (Extra High Tension) cap. Showing great presence of mind, he quickly disconnected the tube, thrust it into a canvas bag, and rushed out of the door, which fortunately gave immediate access on to the sports field. As the tube could have imploded at any time, it was finished off by a hammer being hurled at it, followed by quite an explosion.

"I also saw inside Mr Atkinson's laboratory where some colour television transmissions being received from Alexandra Palace for its time, the quality was somewhat garish and it would be another thirteen years before it would be a public service. I was also given some experimental work to check the tolerance limits of the line hold of the new T161 and its RF circuit sensitivity (as a result of adverse comments raised by Test Engineering) - invariably their engineers were correct! My working hours were cut to thirty-seven and a half hours per week to coincide with other workers in the laboratories.

MONSTRATION THEATRE

1952 Radio Olympia visit by EKCO apprentices. Forth from right is John Brown. (J.Brown)

1952 Radio Olympia - Apprentices' visit conducted by Mr R R Laird, Personnel Manager, and Mr J E Neale, Assistant Personnel Manager (I am fourth from the right).

"In July, an invitation was sent to my parents inviting them to visit the EKCO works at Southend to have a conducted tour, followed by tea with Mr Laird and Mr Neale. Mr Neale said I would be one of the guides, from which I gathered that all parents of first year apprentices had been invited. I learnt later from my parents that before the tour they had expressed surprise to Mr Neale that I would be one of the guides, as they thought I would not have the confidence to do this. They were much heartened when he told them that they might be surprised. At the subsequent tea (at which I was not present), they said how much they had enjoyed the tour and that I had done well. Mr Neale was an excellent judge of young people and I count myself very fortunate that he was responsible for the apprenticeship scheme.

"At the end of August, I was transferred to the car radio laboratory, initially housed in a large hut in the centre of the EKCO site. The laboratory was in the charge of a dour Scotsman, Mr Carlton Chapman, who had been chief engineer of the Rutherglen factory during the war. He had as his assistants George Rolfe and Bob Harvey. The atmosphere was enlivened by the visits to the lab of Ralph Atkinson and Chick Ashley (a Canadian) who were the two area representatives. Ralph was about thirty-five years old, rotund and very urbane; Chick, in his past, had been a lumberjack and was older and a more gritty character. I used to look forward to their visits, as the lab atmosphere was rather serious.

"Sales of EKCO car radios were rather limited as the main competitor was Radiomobile, owned by Smiths, which had the monopoly of the car instrument market, so the company could lean on car manufacturers to recommend Radiomobile. However following a bidding competition, EKCO won the highly prized Ford contract. Pricing was keen and was continually scrutinised by Ford. The CR117, a push-button model with manual tuning, had a size disadvantage compared with the Radiomobile; it would not fit behind the dashboard fascia of many cars. A novel prototype had been developed which used a cam-tuning device to drive the tuning coils, provisionally known as the CR152. Apart from its novel design, it had the great virtue of being shorter in length than the CR117 and would therefore fit all cars. Surprisingly, it was Ford who became interested in the prototype which Mr Toft (general manager of Ford) spotted gathering dust on a shelf in the lab, and he encouraged Mr Chapman to restart development. One of the most difficult areas was the design of the cam for mass production, because plastic mouldings shrink differently and affect the correct tracking of the RF and oscillator circuits. A very serious young engineer, Geoff Oxley, joined the car radio lab about this time and was given the job of designing the coils for the tuning circuits.

"Whilst the CR152 was being developed, Ford had re-designed the Ford Consul, Zephyr, and Zodiac gear-change, and a parcel shelf was introduced under a slimmed-down dashboard. This necessitated a re-styling of the CR117 to sit on the parcel shelf and be finished in black crackle with a black front escutcheon. It looked pretty ugly, but I was given the job of introducing the changes to the radio and seeing in its mass production. Although John Yates in the Drawing Office primarily designed the changes, I encountered a technical problem with the aerial socket, because a grommet I used contained carbon - a lesson I remembered for the rest of my life.

"At about this time, a short-wave converter was designed to work with the CR117, which showed promise, as a cheaper version of the CR61, a model of which was installed in Royal Daimlers. We also on occasions did installations for promotional purposes for special customers, including Eric Winston (the band leader).

"Access to the Rootes Group had been denied to EKCO because of Radiomobiles's favoured position by virtue of the Smiths' monopoly as instrument suppliers; however, I was soon to learn one of my early lessons in the importance of influence. Lord Waleron was on the board of EKCO and it was decided that he should approach Lord Rootes about the possibility of accepting an EKCO CR117 for evaluation trials in the new Hillman Husky that was undergoing development. The suggestion/proposal was favourably received and in order to demonstrate the non-selective nature prior to the trials, a CR117 was chosen at random off the assembly line, and Ralph Atkinson took it to Ryton and installed it in a Hillman Husky. The subsequent evaluation trials were most satisfactory: a direct comparison was made with the Radiomobile. After a punishing trial of the car, the CR117 was apparently the only piece of electrical equipment still functioning at the end. Without any adjustments to the CR117, it was installed in another Husky and the trial repeated. Again, the CR117 continued to function well.

As a direct outcome of these trials, Rootes offered the CR117 as an alternative to the Radiomobile throughout its entire car range. At a later date, the new CR152 became the favoured car radio by Rootes following very similar trials. From time to time, I went to the Ford R & D works, at Rainham, Essex, for trials work, taking lunch at 'The Eastman', or I accompanied Mr Chapman on road trials of car radios to investigate specific aspects. Trolley Bus overhead lines used to give a rhythmic click-click whenever we drove round Southend or Ilford Broadway.

"In early summer of 1952, I was despatched to the CR117 production line urgently: the line had stopped. The problem was microphony in the pentode (EAF42) audio stage. Investigations and comparisons showed that Mullards had brought in from their parent company, Phillips, a changed screen grid construction that was prone to microphony under our test conditions. The solution was to mount the B8A valve base on rubber and change the associated wiring from a single solid core to multiple strand. In July 1952, the CR181/F (Ford's modified CR117 for its new range of Consul, Zephyr, and Zodiac) started being produced on the Southend production line with no problems.

"The following month, I heard that I had passed my S2 of ONC. Each summer, during the college break, EKCO would lay on a varied series of industrial visits to other companies, the Radio Show, as well as the 'Meet the EKCO Management' functions. It was a good company for which to work. In the late summer of 1953, I attained my ONC and was up-graded to Student Apprentice. About this time, it was announced that the Nucleonics Group was moving from Malmesbury to Southend and required two student apprentices. I made known my interest in applying, through Mr Neale, and, in due course, I had an interview with Mr Thompson, the head of nucleonics. He was ex-army with rimless glasses and a ginger moustache. I must have said the right things, as four days later I heard that I had been accepted, together with Ray Steele (who had also just completed his ONC). It was decided I should work in the Medical Applications Section, whose chief was Ernie Hodgson, a delightful rather eccentric character but quite brilliant, and very easy to work for.

"The application of nuclear sources to a variety of fields was in its infancy, so the scope was fascinating. Thickness gauges were being applied to heavy manufacturing production - Carborundum, for instance, had placed a large contract for its Manchester factory, as well as in Canada at Niagara Falls. This was to be a fully automatic system controlled from Ericson Dekatron counting tubes and the monitoring heads switched through NSF Ledex multi-bank switches. An array of coloured lights indicated the status of the whole system.

"The treatment of thyroid cancer was in its infancy in 1953, and a scintillation counter had been developed by EKCO, which helped develop a test in the same year for thyroid cancer which is still used today. In conjunction with a scaler, it plotted a polar diagram of the patient's thyroid, having ingested a barium meal. The pioneering work was carried out with the London Hospital in Whitechapel. The scintillation counter used a sodium iodine crystal, and a large and formidable lady called Miss Hunt grew these in our chemistry laboratory. The crystals were grown in large pint sized Army mugs, which were placed in ovens heated to extremely high temperatures.

"When they were ready, the mug had to be broken to release the hot crystal, which was a hazardous operation as these would splatter fragments in all directions. Miss Hunt complained that these could burn her nylons, so one of the lab assistants had to perform this task - usually Ray or myself in practice! No Health and Safety Regulations in those days. By the autumn of 1953, I had started my HNC (Higher National Certificate), which, as usual, meant one day at college and two evening classes during the week. This involved going home for tea at 6pm, and leaving at 6.30pm to reach Southend by 7pm. Classes finished at 9.30pm, so it was usually home and to bed before another full day.

"Occasionally, the college would lay on a special lecture of technical interest. One particular lecture created great interest: the subject was 'Transistors', which at that time quite unknown to most of us, and the intricacies of point contact and junction types were covered by a scientist from Mullard's. Little did we realise that in a short time electronics would be transformed with the introduction of transistors.

"Among the various amusing memories from my time in nucleonics, two come to mind; both involved testing our exposure to nuclear sources - one legitimate and the other quite the opposite. All personnel working in the department were required to wear a radiation film badge issued by the National Physical Laboratories (NPL) at Teddington. We were given to understand that the badges revealed the amount of blackening in relation to how much exposure experienced over the two-week period. As a further safeguard, a visiting nurse took our blood count. I had not long joined the department when I experienced such a test. I was called in and what looked like a crude scriber (similar to ones we used in the workshops for marking up cutting lines) was punched into my small finger. As no blood appeared, this action was repeated several times, until I remembered nothing else. I was later told that the nurse rushed out to seek Mr Thompson's assistance with the cry,

'One of the young apprentices has passed out'. I realised later that the finger she had selected was deficient in blood from an accident I had had some years earlier. I got my leg well pulled after that performance.

"The other incident concerned an engineer who was known as a lazy individual. This chap very cunningly placed his film badge inside the safe where all radiation sources were stored over a weekend. On the following Monday, having retrieved the film badge, he handed it in to the Safety Officer for the normal two weekly collection. Two days later Mr Thompson received an urgent telephone call from Teddington advising him that one of his staff had apparently been exposed to very high radiation, and that the person concerned should immediately go to Southend General Hospital for blood checks. Not surprisingly, the results were normal, but on medical advice a period off work of six weeks was recommended. It was only when the individual tried (most unwisely) for a second time that his ruse was finally rumbled and he was sacked.

"Examinations time came round as rapidly as usual - this time for A1 of the HNC in June. Whilst I was waiting for the results, I was asked if I would like to do an exchange with another student apprentice from the factory at Malmesbury. The first part of the exchange was for John Solly to come to stay at my home for two weeks and work at the main Southend factory. I found John to be a very quiet, diffident person and difficult to entertain as his interests did not coincide with mine. It seemed a long two weeks. A few weeks later it was my turn to go to Malmesbury. The journey down was by train to Swindon, and from there in the factory staff car, driven by a lady who had driven ambulances in London during the war. She was a brilliant driver; roads in that part of Wiltshire were full of twists and turns, but I never felt safer - it changed my opinion of lady drivers.

"Malmesbury had originally been purchased at the beginning of the Second World War as a shadow factory. At the centre of the site was 'Cowbridge House', a very attractive country house, and the research and development staffs and production teams had been accommodated in the stables and the wartime factory buildings around the site. After the changeover from wartime to peacetime, the site continued to develop airborne radar - but now for the new Bristol Britannia and Comet civil airliners. Very compact (for those days) military trans-receivers were also being developed and I remember participating in the field trials in the grounds of Cowbridge House, during my short stay with the radio section. I was also attached to one of the radar departments working on a Ministry of Supply contract code called 'Blue Sky Radar' for the RAF.

"With the finals of HNC out of the way, I could start to enjoy the summer and the EKCO visits programme once took us to De Havilland at Hatfield to see the new Comet 4 being built for BOAC and other overseas airlines. I also did a day on the EKCO stand at the Physical Society Exhibition at the Royal Horticultural Hall, and where a new piece of equipment I had helped to engineer was being shown for the first time. At this stage of my life, I was nearly twenty-two and as the autumn of 1955 arrived, I was starting to become restless. I had successfully completed my five-year apprenticeship and I would normally be expected to complete my graduate-ship examinations over the next year as EKCO had been granted deferment of my National Service as I was employed on a Ministry contract for AWRE (Atomic Energy Research Establishment) at Harwell. However, five years of examinations immediately following on from school was becoming monotonous and I wanted a change. I decided to throw up my deferment and get my National Service out of the way - I did not realise this would mean even more examinations but that's another story."

Dave Wiggins, (employed 1962-1970)

"I began working as a young teenager at EKCO as a 'lab boy' on a year's trial in the home market Television Design Lab under the supervision of Ted Maynard, John Davis and George Barsealman. Following this, I was taken on as an apprentice' in the radio and television section under a scheme sponsored by the EEF (Engineering Employers Federation), which consisted of being indentured in one of three grades, namely Craft, Technical and Student. I was graded as a Technical Apprentice on the grand sum of £4 pounds and 10 shillings a week, which was a nice rise from my £3 per week as a 'lab boy'.

"As far as I can remember, all of my 'Technical Apprentice' colleagues also worked in the various design labs within the Development and Engineering Block (known to all as Dev & Eng) or the front research labs (the Wells Coates designed building). The craft apprentices were mostly employed either in the factory or the maintenance areas and the student apprentices (of which there were very few) were seconded to the company by the universities and worked in the labs. Other than at the final presentation of my indenture, I do not recall ever meeting any of the EKCO Craft apprentices although I did get to know two students in the Avionics Microwave Lab, one being Bob Puttock and the other Paddy Melvin.

"Both of these lads were undoubtedly very gifted academically but seemed to know 'ought about nought' (as our northern friends say) in terms of practical skills. I often wonder where these lads ended up once they got their degrees.

I came to join the Avionics Division by a piece of bad luck, this being the transfer of all the television design unit to Pye Ltd at Lowestoft. Staff and senior staff were offered the chance to relocate and were taken by coach to Lowestoft to view the Pye factory. Apprentices were not offered the opportunity to relocate. The apprentice supervisor - a Mr Budd - asked me where I'd like to work and it was more or less left to me to find someone who would take on my remaining period of apprenticeship. Here I got lucky, instead of me having to punt around, an engineer came looking for me.

"He was Major Stan Brown (REME retired) who EKCO Avionics had employed after his military retirement to upgrade and run a small test equipment calibration cell within the radar labs; its function being to introduce some decent standards of accurate measurement vis-à-vis military contracts. I took to Stan, who had worked at MoD 'Aquilla' (a testing facility in Bromley, Kent) at once and said 'yes please' to the avionics offer.

"After a short interview and a welcome from VJ Cox, my papers were transferred and I began to train in test and measurement. Stan Brown proved to be a stickler for accuracy and my training was thorough. I was soon calibrating the lab's stock of test-meters and 'oscilloscopes' - an experience that was to stand me in good stead in my later career with the MoD where I managed similar calibration labs myself. When my five year papers expired in 1968, I was asked to move on yet again.

"Again I got lucky as the engineer who ran the environmental testing for the 'radar' teams, Ron Lee, had asked for a technician with an electronics bias as he was a mechanical engineer. As I had gained some experience in the environmental testing field during my earlier apprenticeship years in the 'TV' design labs, I applied and was accepted as a staff R&D electronics technician and there was lots to do! EKCO had just built a dedicated Environmental Test Laboratory in the central car park adjacent to the Dev and Eng building, which caused some problems since this was built over one of the wartime underground shelters, necessitating one of the old entrances being filled in and extra deep foundations. The building also had to be specially designed to accommodate the vibration cell, which had a brand new Pye/LING shaker set over a large concrete pit; this being driven by a B&O swept sine wave waveform generator and a huge Pye valve power amplifier.

"To contain the sound waves from the vibration table the walls were specially insulated, the roof was made of a 'Thermcoustic' sound deadening material and the doors were also soundproofed. The building had two large rooms, one for the vibration table and the second room for the Barlow-Whitney environmental test chambers where equipment could be tested over a temperature range of -50°C to plus 70°C, up to 100 percent humidity and a simulated altitude of up to 50,000 ft. Testing of radar scanners and transmitter/receivers (commonly known as T/R's) were sometimes of 24-hour duration and needed late working. Living close by in Prittlewell (closer than where Ron lived in Rochford) meant that I tended to get the calls from the EKCO security box, such as: 'We passed your building and its making a VERY loud noise – can you come and have a look?' The worst I can remember was at 10pm one night when I found a shattered scanner hanging over the edge of the shaker, while the oscillator happily kept sweeping through the frequency band! Such is R&D work.

"We worked under the direct input of the design staff of course. The chief mechanical design engineer was a rather eccentric man called Mr Gibson who was well known as something of a character (to say the least) and was commonly referred to as 'Gibby'. My impression was that he'd been designing scanner dishes all his life – but he could still get it wrong as evidenced on the day we ran the first vibration test on his prototype E-390 scanner destined for Concorde. Put simply, it just fell apart bit by bit, which caused 'Gibby' to chuckle but VJ Cox (head of design) and Phil Stride (the MD) who were both observers were not amused. In fact I seem to remember that they both went pale as so much hung on the project. Modification upon modification followed until it came good but the cost of the E-390 was huge. I remember taking the same scanner to the Government Environmental Test Centre (ETC), which was part of the weapons test range on Foulness Island for climatic testing. Ron and I had built our own climatic test cabinet to take the 30 inch dish, which was a large wooden box fed by liquid nitrogen or CO_2 depending on the low temperature required.

"High temperature was catered for by banks of old EKCO electric fire elements set in the floor. It was all very 'Heath Robinson' and although it worked the ARB (Air Registration Board - the forerunner of the CAA) decided that the ETC would get the job with Ron and I as observers. I operated the radar as each new temperature was reached and it finally failed at a very low temperature (-80°C, I think), when the scanner froze solid. In later years I was posted to the ETC as part of my MoD career. During the welcome speech the interviewer said 'well of course this will all be new to you David'. He was astonished when I said, 'No, I've been here before – I did a few years in environmental testing of radar sets!!' I went on to serve there for eight not very happy years as a MoD Technical Officer keeping an eye on contractors.

"The Avionics Environmental Lab catered for the full range of temperature, humidity and vibration test although we had no centrifuge or shock tower, with these tests being sub-contacted - centrifuge testing going to RRE Malvern for example. We were also able to use equipment owned by

EKCO Radio and TV. In case you think that such extreme testing is only necessary for aviation equipment, this is not so. One of the reasons that EKCO TV/Radios, etc, were so highly regarded by the trade and customers almost from the beginning of the company was the test laboratory set up by Richard Spencer in the 1930s, where ably assisted by his lifelong assistant Miss Pam Durrent, he introduced high and low temperature, humidity and 'life testing' for all components and sets prior to them going into production. The finished sets were also randomly tested since EKCO recognised that they were sold in parts of the world where conditions were not the same as the UK. Another example of the thoroughness of EKCO design was the fact that an anechoic chamber was set up to test loudspeaker design and acoustic quality. Spencer of course being an accomplished musician took a great interest in this area but the audio side was under Clive Fisher.

"A severe limitation of the lab's vibration capability was our inability to carry out 'random noise' testing since the B&O generator was sine wave only. At the time I was there, 'random noise' testing was being written into the relevant British Standard (BS) specifications and so we had to obtain individual ARB (CAA) waivers for 'sine' testing. I have no knowledge of what was done about this when the lab was moved to Crawley, but by then the shaker controller was already obsolete (1970-71).

"The last radar system I tested was the E-90 'baby' radar whose type approval I did a lot of work on. This work included writing the ARB (CAA) type approval document – something I'd not done before. I understood at the time that the company was looking to sell this very lightweight weather radar to the emerging market of small corporate aircraft such as the Learjet and the Hawker Siddeley HS125, etc. I am not sure if any were actually sold but it is unlikely since the American giant electronics firms such as Bendix, Collins and Raytheon, had the executive jet market pretty much to themselves. Older established equipment like the E-190 and 'Red Steer' (the 'V' Bomber tail warning radar) also came back to our lab for re-assessment to higher standards. I recall my amazement at seeing that the latter was entirely valve operated, such was its age by then. To me, as a newly qualified electronics engineer brought up on transistors, it was out of the ark.

"I've subsequently learned that 'Red Steer' actually soldiered on until 1992 when the last of the 'V' bombers was retired and Red Steer operated in the tail of XM607 during operation 'Black Buck' – the bombing of Port Stanley airfield during the Falklands conflict. Talking of obsolete, all of our prototype equipment was test flown in the company Anson ('PG' in my time) and I had the good fortune to do a couple of these test flights assisting I think (Dennis) Williams who worked in Post Design Services) The poor old girl seemed to stagger up to 5,000 feet after entertaining the Aviation Traders ground crew with its huge sheets of flame from the engines on start-up. Years later, in discussion with one of these chaps, he told me they were not so much admiring the old girl but wondering if she'd make it off the runway one more time!

"When I left I did hear a rumour that the company was considering buying a Beech replacement, but the problem was the need to fit the thirty-inch scanner dish from the E-390 in the nose. I enjoyed my five-year apprenticeship at EKCO and my six years at Southend Technical College, even though life in the laboratories was hard at times especially when I was given every rotten job going, mistreated, abused and paid rotten money. BUT I got to work for and be taught by some truly amazing top engineers who generously passed on their life's experience to me – something I tried to emulate when later it became my turn to train apprentices. Looking back all these years and long retired, the EKCO training was unbeatable. It set me up for a life in engineering just as it was meant to do. I would not have swapped it for anything and I would have stayed on longer given the chance. I consider that I had the very best of the years from 1962 to 1970 even through the firm was failing as I started out. Within my decade as a young 'tech' and in my sight – the world of truly modern electronics was being born – high definition (625-line) and colour TV where I was privileged to work in the very next room to the colour design lab and saw first-hand the first 'CT' series/625-line, NTSC and PAL sets trialled.

"The first TV remote controls, portable TV sets, the first 'compact cassettes' and 8-track cassette players, car radios moving from high voltage valves to low voltage transistors, ever smaller and smaller portable transistor radios, stereo and quad sound systems, better and better semiconductors, smaller and smaller passive components, printed circuits, the first 'chips', miniature everything, lower voltages and lighter weight. EKCO lead in many of these fields and it was a privilege to work in such a design hothouse and with such inventive people, so how did it all go so wrong? The ill-judged merger with Pye did not help although at our level we did not know much of the 'ins and outs' of this. What we did know was that the E-390 Concorde radar was a drain, under resourced and it must have been a burden for Avionics' to weather. The bigger picture was that even in the mid-1960s the UK Radio and TV industry was starting to be overwhelmed by cheap imports and not helped by weak government. This is my opinion of course. " (Dave Wiggins, 2009)

Chapter 11

End Of An Era

With such monumental success and growth of EKCO, it came as a huge surprise that towards the end of 1960, the company's founder Eric Cole suddenly entered into a merger with Pye Ltd of Cambridge. Here for the first time his son Derek provides an insight into that decision and of his father's wishes to preserve the company at any cost.

Derek Cole:

"I was not a director and knew nothing of the merger plans until about two months later. My reaction was that some such deal was very urgent. I knew the EKCO Finance Director had managed to borrow £1 million from Mercantile Credit (on the golf course, he said) this had to be repaid fairly quickly and my father was clearly faced with a rerun of the 1932 situation. Mortgaging his home in Marlow would not save the situation this time. He had to act quickly and Charles Orr Stanley, MD of Pye, later said that it was in June/July 1960, in fact almost at once, that they provisionally agreed the merger. 'Why on earth Pye?' I asked. One director said to me that my father had repeatedly referred to Pye's way of working, as so alien to EKCO. My mother from time to time whispered to me things my father, a very secretive man, kept to himself. Earlier c1959 she had said, 'Your father is all uneasy because Jules Thorn is talking of a consolidation of the Industry.' Why then not Thorn? [1]

---

[1] There were about 28 other UK electronics manufacturers at the time, and Thorn was one of the biggest.

"My father did say he had thought a merger with Pye, bigger but not overwhelmingly bigger than EKCO, was the only way he could give the top EKCO management the opportunity of a meaningful future. It seems to me inevitable that as soon as the scale of the crisis hit him in June 1960 he consulted Derek Pritchard, as he always did. It is likely he was assured that Stanley would certainly value and make proper use of the EKCO management, whose contracts had been extended. Stanley did indeed, in an unpredictable manner, give great scope for some but not all he employed. He shared my father's sense of debt to his colleagues, but in his case he side-lined those he rejected and they held sinecure positions. He was too kind-hearted to move them out.

"My father thought that any major company making a hostile take-over, as was very likely, would trample on the existing management, but that Pye would still give them scope. In that he succeeded. There was nothing surreptitious about it. Nothing could be done unless the full EKCO board agreed the merger. Given the sudden crisis in the TV industry in 1960, they must have been VERY relieved that somebody would agree a merger. The board presumably were uncomfortably aware that they had not taken any steps to deal with this until my father returned after four months in a Swiss hospital. The Works Superintendent later said to me, 'Only the directors didn't know what the situation was'.

"The April 1960 financial report by EKCO's Finance Director, John Corbishley, had made it plain that independent existence was no longer possible, although he didn't say so. Corbishley's financial report of April 1961, written after the merger, showed an even worse situation. It was a merger at law, in that the shareholders of both companies were invited and agreed to accept shares in British Electronic Industries (BEI) in exchange for shares. Stanley later renamed BEI as 'Pye of Cambridge'. The controlling directors were: Stanley; his brother E.J. (known at Pye as 'The Director for the West Indies', where he lived); Mr Hawkins formerly of Pye's electrical heating subsidiary, Hawkins of Hastings; together with my father and Corbishley. The merger documents were approved by the full EKCO board under the personal supervision of the most eminent company solicitor in London, David Jennings of Allen & Overy, and fully complied with the Companies Act. However the author Mark Frankland revealed in his book 'Radio Man', that Pye's auditors complained they were kept out of the preparation of Pye's contribution.

"My father and Stanley agreed that they would each go on running their own show. When the further decline of the industry made this unsound, my father said to me in August 1961, that he and Stanley ought to hand over executive power of BEI to a new managing director from outside, with the two of them stepping back. I do not know if he ever put this to Stanley. I suggested at once that Rupert Jones, the outstanding figure among the Pye and EKCO boards, should be appointed. (This was the solution adopted by Phillips five years later. Rupert was appointed by Stanley to take over EKCO when we left and he brought it rapidly back into profit. Before the 1966 AGM, he invited me in and gave his account of the chaos at Pye.)

"My father transferred the trademark EKCO and any associated copyright to the new private company in 1926 as a major part of his investment. Billy Verrells put in his know-how and expertise. Maxwell, Manners and Pring put in the new capital. I don't know the exact proportions for sure but I always assumed it was 20% of the shares each. However the company as a 'legal person', not the shareholders, owned all copyrights. The Pye merger documents disclosed that by 1960 my father owned only 3% of the EKCO shares."

Sales of EKCO radios and televisions slumped in 1961 due to overcapacity, although transistor portable sales remained good. Still, Eric Cole was uneasy with the way the merger was working to the detriment of EKCO.

"My father stopped drawing his salary when at the time of the April 1960 report the crisis looked serious and drew nothing until he resigned about 18 months later. His contract was expiring before the merger and he did not ask for it to be renewed. He had always refused to draw his annual bonus, fixed originally for a small company pre-war. He refused Stanley's offer of a Golden Handshake on the grounds that in the crisis the company couldn't afford it.

"The EKCO board accepted my father's suggestion that they and all senior executives should have their contracts renewed before the merger. When Stanley said in effect he was going to do the joint managing director's job himself, I suggested we approach Hawkins to see if he would support the appointment of Rupert Jones or an outsider as managing director. Failing that I asked my father if he would launch an American style 'proxy war' to get his team elected to the board at the AGM.

"He said tersely, 'No. That would make things worse. The crisis is too serious already. The group will not survive a divided leadership. I must go'. It was at that point and not at the merger itself that he stood down."

In fact, Cole and his son Derek resigned from both the joint and the separate EKCO board, thus severing his association with the company that had bore his name since 1926. Reporting a large drop in profits of the group, Stanley, in his annual report laid the blame squarely on the EKCO acquisition. It was to ultimately be the demise of two leading firms. EKCO and Pye were still trading as separate entities with their own products in 1962. However, from the EKCO perspective, many of the engineers who had been instrumental in the development and growth of the business were approaching retirement age and as these retired, they were not replaced.

"It may surprise people but Stanley had the reputation of being very kind hearted and never sacked anybody. There were men at Cambridge doing 'advisory' non-jobs provided they didn't oppose him. As a result of the merger, EKCO was back to normal by 1963 and I wrote to Rupert Jones, Pye's Director-in-Charge, to congratulate him. The subsequent collapse of the entire UK TV industry was due to different macro-economic influences.

"After leaving the business, my father burnt his personal papers. All company documents were at Southend. My mother and I were quite clear that as a deeply private man he was horrified at the thought of his life being publicised. I am afraid he would be absolutely furious a book is being published - and with me for helping with it! He did however retain copies of various current documents, including the Corbishley reports. I made them available to Frankland and they are now at Southend Museum.

"I also still have my father's press cutting of the Hague Congress of 1948, which he helped to finance. Today, the EU has fulfilled what Winston Churchill said was his most important hope, to 'restore the economic life of Germany and revive the ancient fame of the German race without exposing their neighbours to any reassertion of their military power...' My father was one of a group of Conservative businessmen who in January 1949 funded the new UK European Movement under Churchill's presidency.

"The ratification by Parliament in February 1951 of the European Convention of Human Rights (ECHR) was the first reward for my father in response to his personal expenditure and activity in the European Movement designed to secure his great passion for a permanent continental peace. I went on my father's behalf to Strasbourg for the next meeting, where this proposal of

Eric Cole signing Kruger and Wilson anti-apartheid agreement with Boris Wilson, March 1957. (D.Cole).

Churchill's was adopted to introduce to war-torn Europe British standards of Liberty. The great Conservative Home Secretary, Maxwell Fife, drafted it and the Conservatives used an Opposition Day in February 1951 to force it through the Commons, despite the doubts of the Labour Government.

"Newsreel of the 1958 UKEM conference on the abortive negotiations for a Free Trade Area shows Sir Edward Beddington Behrens welcoming the Chancellor. Behrens was my father's financial adviser and close friend who had launched EKCO on the stock exchange. I was waiting inside as Sir Edward's PA for the four days of the conference.

"The British Prime Minister, David Cameron, said in January 2013, 'The first purpose of the European Union – to secure peace – has been achieved and we should pay tribute to all those in the EU who made that happen.' In doing so, he paid generous tribute to Conservatives like my father for their devoted belief in the European cause. The ECHR was their first success.

"As a young law student, I was fascinated by the adoption by Maxwell Fife, the Nuremburg Prosecutor, of our Bill of Rights 1689 as the basis for the ECHR. Clause 5 prohibiting 'cruel and unusual punishments', later included in the Irish and American Constitutions, was expanded to prohibit evidence gathered by torture and it is a great step forward that it is now established that nobody in Britain who has travelled abroad can be extradited or deported to face such evidence.

"Churchill would be astonished that this British inspired Convention is now in force from Vladivostok to the Azores and is being used in court by 25000 Russians to overturn Stalin's laws. My father, as a lifelong Conservative passionately devoted to a Europe at peace, would surely call the ECHR the greatest achievement of the Conservative Party since the war."

Pye in the Sky

The formation of British Electronic Industries Ltd (BEI) thus effectively ended EKCO's thirty-five years of independent trading. A joint board of directors was formed to manage the merger, although for day-to-day running of both companies separate boards were maintained. It certainly did not have the support of the EKCO board, but the rationale was that most families already owned a radio and the market was over supplied. Development work commenced on UHF televisions with 625-lines, following the government decision that this will be the future-broadcasting standard - this encompassed both black and white and colour television. The E-190 weather radar entered service with British European Airways as its launch customer, and the first prototype 'helicopter radar' began test trials. EKCO then won the contract to develop the weather radar for Concorde in 1965. The Nucleonics Group also began installing control room instrumentation at the Magnox nuclear power stations.

A year later, colour televisions in NTSC, PAL and SECAM formats were developed, but since no decision had been made as to which format would be adopted, EKCO, like all the other television manufacturers, had to be ready for production once the decision was taken, but in the meantime, consumers were waiting and not buying. The decision that 625-line transmission would be the standard to be adopted in the UK meant that sales of black and white 405-line televisions went flat, and stockpiles began to build up at EKCO.

The company was further hit by the loss of a 'Schools TV' contract as well as the hoped-for contract to sell sets to South Africa fell through due to the government embargo of goods to that country. However, sales picked up once dual standard 405/625-line sets began to be produced. The 625-line standard television sets entered production in 1964, in anticipation of the launch of BBC Two. The E-290 weather radar system also began production, with flight trials beginning on helicopter radar, and the Medical Counting laboratories developed a colour-imaging scanner for thyroid conditions in the form of a small Anger-type gamma camera, the first steps towards the MRI scanners used today. Development work also began on Miss Distance Indicating System (MDI) for the Royal Aircraft Establishment (RAE) at Farnborough.

Pye, which had also been producing a wide range of domestic appliances, including televisions and radios, had, since the merger with EKCO, expanded into many areas such as telephone exchanges, scientific instruments, and marine radio equipment. In the field of medical electronics, they were also world leaders in spectrophotometry.[1]

The Pye television studio equipment, notably the cameras, did well in international sales, and was very popular with British broadcasters including the BBC. The Pye Mk6 Image Orthicon camera was the last version supplied to BBC outside broadcasts in 1963 for a new fleet of eight outside broadcast vans. The ITV companies purchased the popular Pye Mk3 studio cameras, but unfortunately Pye never made it into producing a colour broadcast television camera, except for an abortive colour Telecine camera, and few, if any, were sold. Pye didn't have the money to plough into the technology, and were not ready by the time the test signals began in 1966.

In February 1966, an interim report from Pye stated that sales had dropped by a third, and profits for the group would be £478,000 against the 1964 value of £2.27 million. Pye issued an announcement that despite poor sales, the three Essex factories were safe from closure. On 20th May 1966, in a shock announcement, 800 workers at Priory Crescent were told they would lose their jobs with immediate effect, as part of a restructuring plan by Pye, and that television and radio manufacture would move away from Southend.

The company's profits largely depended on domestic sales of radios and televisions, and the dual standard sets (405 and 625-line) proved to be technically challenging, as they were virtually two sets in one, costing more to produce. Plus, it was becoming increasingly popular for people to rent a television than buy one, not least because of their chronic unreliability. John Stanley had reported to the Pye board in 1962 that as many as four out of every five television sales were to rental companies such as Domestic Electric Rentals (DER) and Radio Rentals.

Pye, like many other domestic manufacturers, was also in competition with cheaper Japanese imports and this impacted on demand for British-built items. Consumers preferred the cheaper colour televisions launched by Sony and Hitachi, and with a wider choice over price and quality in the market, domestic manufacturers found themselves with high stocks and low cash flow at a time when industrial relations were poor and there was little flexibility in cost

---

[1] Spectrophotometry is a photometer which can measure intensity as a function of the light source wavelength, its features being spectral bandwidth and linear range of absorption or reflectance measurement.

reduction. Pye did attempt to restore demand with strong price competition, and sold excess stock at a loss. But the tactic had no strategic value, and by 1966, Pye was in such difficulties that they started to reduce their manufacturing capacity, the biggest loss being the closure of the EKCO factory in Southend. Television production was moved to a little-used Pye factory in Lowestoft and radio production was moved to a Pye factory in Cambridge, which left the assembly hall at Southend empty and silent for the first time (except for the wartime work) since 1930. Of the staff remaining, most were re-allocated to either the plastics (later known as Lin Pac Mouldings Ltd) or electronics departments both of which were now 'stand-alone businesses'. Television sales remained depressed, although portable transistor radio sales remained good - partly as a result of a new trend in 'pirate radio'.

End of an Era

Having lost control of his company, Eric was to suffer an even greater loss, when his wife Muriel died suddenly, aged 59, in July 1965. She had not been well since a serious stomach operation in 1953. In the early years of the business, Muriel had been an invaluable asset to him and the business, and was responsible for all the accounts and administration, thus allowing Eric to concentrate on developing products. In grief for his life-long partner, he was also mourning the demise of his life's work. Meanwhile, a financial scandal was threatening to engulf Pye.

"It was caused by a disagreement over the bad debt potential resulting from sales to a rental company in which Pye had only a minority interest, coupled with problems with the reliability of the rented sets. This arose because Stanley adopted a low-cost tuner against Tony Martin's advice. This unreliable tuner had a wider effect and on top of very poor sales figures, caused a boardroom row and an accountant's investigation was ordered. Stanley resigned and his son was sacked. Quite suddenly, the whole Pye/EKCO business was ripe for take-over and eventually bought by Philips, making it the UK's biggest exporter of television and radio. In the wings Jules Thorn was watching with interest."

The demise of EKCO's founder was also sudden. It took Eric sometime after Muriel's death to decide what to do. He had been a chairman of Robinson Rentals since around 1962: The owner, David Robinson, wanted to cash in on his 100 percent holding of Robinson Rentals without surrendering control, so he consulted Jules Thorn, who made his sets.

Thorn told him that if he sold a minority interest (around 35 percent) he needed a chairman of high reputation to satisfy the stock exchange to protect the minority, and Eric Cole was the obvious choice. In theory he was not an active executive but stood in for David Robinson when during an 18 month period the founder spent most of his time fishing in Scotland. Cole worked as required from his private London flat. Cole then toured the USA and South Africa, before retiring to live first in an apartment in the Royal Garden Hotel in London and then in St Kitts Village, Barbados, where he and Muriel had enjoyed holidays. It was here that while swimming on 18 November 1966, Eric Cole died aged 65.

"He couldn't swim, but he went out into the long shallows at St James', Barbados, on the Atlantic side, where the tidal rise there is only a few feet. He died as a result of 'Vagal Inhibition'. This is a condition that causes sudden death to occur within seconds or a minute or two, due to minor trauma or relatively simple and harmless peripheral stimulation, e.g., shock. I was thirty-five years old at the time, and received a phone call from his bank manager in Barbados to tell me the news. I was due to fly out the next day to report on the chaotic Pye Annual General Meeting, which had taken place the day before. My father's body was returned to the UK for cremation at Southend.

"Jules had arranged to spend Christmas with my father in Barbados to debate possibilities. My father's sudden death halted this. Jules at his funeral questioned me on the value of EKCO assets, but I couldn't really help. He did not proceed.

"During the funeral service, which took place on 29 November 1966, Canon Stanley, said that Eric Cole was "essentially a humble man, who, when asked about his business success commented, 'You know I've never been particularly good at anything but I've succeeded by having around me able men.'"

Although both a plaque was erected and a rose was planted to his memory, unfortunately these were removed in 2000. It is assumed that Lloyds, as executors, booked a plaque as a matter of routine when paying for the funeral out if his estate and payments ran out. Therefore, apart from a portrait painting hanging in the EKCO Social and Sports Club (ESSC) clubhouse, there is no tangible memorial to Eric Cole in Southend.

Kenway Works Assembly Line , 1952
(C.Poole)

Chapter 12

The Rest Of The Story 1967-2008

Philips Electrical Industries emerged with the controlling interest in the Pye-EKCO business in 1967, and cosmetically restyled Philips products appeared under these two brands. The electronics division was split into three parts and merged with the equivalent section of Pye. The radar team joined with the communications team of Pye to become EKCO Avionics, the second team became EKCO Instruments and the third team became EKCO Nucleonic.

After the television and radio production vacated the main Southend assembly hall, work commenced on refurbishing the hall. By the end of 1967 it had a 'clean room' for the assembly of the optical system for the helicopter radar system, as well as production of all the other product lines from Rochford. In addition, a lab was set up for 'thick/thin' film devices (the forerunner to integrated circuits), which had started at Rochford as pioneering work. These were originally developed for the Concorde radar but they also found a home in the Crane Safe Load Indicating system, which had been developed by EKCO Instruments.

At this time the factory at Kenway, Prittlewell was still manufacturing car radios, and Egan on Canvey Island was still producing electrical components as well as domestic and industrial plastic mouldings. At Malmesbury, the heating division was still intact, as was the Warmglow 'electric blanket' site at the 'Somerton' Works along Prince Avenue (the A127) in Westcliff-on-Sea.

In February 1968, the move began to relocate the 550 electronics production staff from Rochford to the refurbished assembly hall at Priory Crescent, thus joining the research and development already on the site. The Rochford site was subsequently closed, offered for sale and bought by 'Lesney Brothers' - the makers of Matchbox toys.

However, it was evident that despite promises and investment from Philips, areas of the refurbished factory remained empty although the 'Pye Westminster taxi radio' was brought in to provide extra work. This was not a success since the staff, who were used to the high grade quality and precision work of military projects, could not easily adapt to the much lower 'commercial' standard of this radio. According to the Southend Standard of February 1968, the total number of EKCO employees in the Southend area at this time was around 3,100. At Malmesbury, the business became Pye TMC (telephone manufacturing company) specialising in the design and manufacture of small company switchboards and exchanges.

In 1969, the only part of the Priory Crescent site looking healthy was 'plastics' with the rest of the site limping along, although there were two projects of interest: Miss Distance Indicators (MDI) and Crane Safe Load Indicators (SLI). MDI were selling well and work was well ahead through the use of 'thin film' and later microchips to miniaturise SLI, which became 'Microgard'. The E-390 weather radar designed for Concorde was delivered to both Toulouse and Filton in time for the first test flights of Concorde 001 (F-WTSS) in March 1969, and of 002 (G-BSST) a month later.

In 1970, there was a sharp downturn in both civil and military aviation sales, which resulted in Philips making plans to relocate the 'avionics' work to another Philips company (MEL) and move 'instruments' into the development and engineering block. During the year a program of redundancies began, resulting in the business being run by a skeleton staff. By the end of 1971, the final moves had been made, and the factory, the offices and the Wells Coates research and development block were empty, and up for sale.

The nuclear and medical parts of EKCO Instruments were sold off to 'Nuclear Enterprises', a company based in Edinburgh, with elements of the medical split between Baldwin Instruments and EMI (Wells).The Industrial Division became CEI (Cambridge Electronic Industries) under the Philips banner but after a short while, this in turn was sold to the Morgan Crucible Company becoming Morganite Electronic Instruments.

In 1972, the empty buildings in Priory Crescent were bought by the Joint Credit Card Company, and following refurbishment and alteration became the 'ACCESS' credit card centre. The site was sectioned off so that EKCO Plastics could operate as a stand-alone business, and another Philips company, London Carriers, moved onto the plastics site.

An unexpected success in the early 1970's was the 'Hostess' heated trolley and tray, which became a 'must have' household accessory and was sold widely. These were made by the Hawkins electrical business of Pye, which traded as EKCO Hawkins Ltd.

The brand name EKCO remained in the market place until 1982 as Philips manufactured transistor radios made in Hong Kong and the Far East, and the televisions coming out of Lowestoft still had the EKCO badge affixed to them although they were essentially Pye designed.

Of the rest of the former EKCO sites, Kenway closed when car radio production ceased. The Somerton works, which had become the home for electric blankets closed when the product fell out of fashion following adverse publicity regarding their safety, and the rise in interest in continental duvets. Egan Electrical continued trading up to 1982 when it was sold to Belling-Leigh.

EKCO Plastics continued trading until the early 1980s when 'Linpac' bought it out. It was subsequently sold on a couple of times further and the last owners were 'Eco-mold', which operated on the original site until its demolition in 2008.

The Malmesbury Pye-TMC site, trading under the Philips umbrella, remained operational until 1984 when Philips entered a joint venture with AT&T to create AT&T and Philips Telecommunications. Known as APT Philips, it gradually transferred its stake in the joint venture to AT&T, with the result that by 1990, AT&T wholly owned the company.

In 1996, AT&T was split into three divisions, and as part of the manufacturing organisation, the company in Cowbridge found itself part of Lucent Technologies. A period of rapid expansion followed with Lucent Technologies growing to occupy numerous sites in Wiltshire and its UK headquarters moving to Swindon.

Following a decline in telecommunications industry the Cowbridge site finally closed in 2002 leaving the once country house to fall into disrepair, resulting in it being demolished at the beginning of 2007. The site was redeveloped for housing and small businesses.

At Priory Crescent, the main site (by now known as the Prittlebrook Trading Estate) was vacated in 2003 when Royal Bank of Scotland (RBS) relocated to a purpose built office block, and FDR (First Data Resources), which manufactured the cards, relocated to Basildon. The site has since stood empty and somewhat like Cowbridge been left to slowly decay away.

Cowbridge House (C.Poole)

Chapter 13

A Very Secret Place: Cowbridge House

E K Cole had a secret which remained a closely guarded 'Top Secret' for the whole of the Second World War, and even into the 1950s and 60s. This was a secret factory, hidden in a country house just outside Malmesbury, Wiltshire, where the wartime manufacture of AI (Airborne Interception) radar for the night fighter force, and ASV (Anti Surface Vessel) radar for Coastal Command and the Fleet Air Arm took place.

In the winter of 1938-39, Eddie 'Taffy' Bowen, one of the brilliant scientists at the radar research establishment at Bawdsey, on the Suffolk coast, had developed airborne radar to a workable stage. To make this reliable and suitable for production, he needed the support and engineering expertise of industry, and so EKCO (along with Pye of Cambridge) were approached. Research and development commenced at the EKCO works in Southend-on-Sea in the spring of 1939, where in a top-secret laboratory, the company threw their considerable expertise into putting the equipment into production.

In August 1939, with war imminent, Michael Lipman (now manager of the electrical appliance division of EKCO) was awoken early one Saturday morning to attend an important meeting at the factory at 8am. There he found the top directors together with three Royal Air Force officers in uniform, and an official in civilian clothes, who was introduced as Group Captain Hugh Leedham. Lipman was requested to leave forthwith and find a factory premises capable of producing radio equipment within a 100 miles radius of the west of London. While not specified, it was implied that the equipment would be of dimensions not greater than television sets.

He was further instructed that on approval of the premises of his choosing they were to be equipped with sufficient machines and tools to enable him to organise production of this unspecified equipment, utilising not more than 200 people. In the event of war he could recruit a nucleus of staff at not higher than foreman level from the main works at Southend-on-Sea.

Lipman immediately set off in search of suitable premises and after several fruitless days narrowed the search down to three or four possible sites, which were textile factories in and about the Stroud Valley. By this time, Germany was on the point of invading Poland. A telephone call to the Air Ministry confirmed the utmost urgency of the search and to this was added the instruction to keep clear of towns due to the need to maintain total secrecy. At the end of the week with the new instructions from the Air Ministry ringing in his ears, he decided to rethink his strategy began to look for a large country house, with possibilities of adaptation and extension, but sufficiently near a centre of population from which to draw labour.

After a new search, he identified a country house within two miles of Malmesbury in Wiltshire. This was Cowbridge House, an 18th century house set in fourteen acres of rolling countryside close to the banks of the river Avon, which meant that industrial water was available as was electrical power from its own water powered generator. The estate came complete with numerous outbuildings including six cottages, and Lipman knew straight away that this was the place. The house and estate were promptly purchased for £6,500 cash.

Work started immediately in converting the house and outbuildings while at the same time making sure that to all intents and purposes the property still looked like a country house. The services of a local builder were employed, and within six to eight weeks, internal walls had been knocked down, ceilings propped up with girders, and space provided for assembly and testing facilities on the ground and first floors of the original house, with office facilities on the upper floors. The Coil Winding Department was installed in the living quarters, beyond the stable yard, originally used by the gardeners and other outside staff. A machine shop was housed in a new building incorporating stables. The old stables, on the banks of the river Avon were converted into a plating and paint spraying shop and a new power main was connected to the local grid with two feeders in case of supply interruption, finally the generator in the water mill was put in order, for emergency lighting - which was never needed. By Christmas 1939, conversion work was complete and four or five large rooms were equipped with benches all wired up ready for radio assembly, although incredibly Lipman, who was designated to be the general manager at Malmesbury, still had no idea what the site was to be used for.

While the conversion work was going on, word went out to the various EKCO 'repair centres' around the country that skilled electricians were needed and staff recruitment began; at the time they were hired they were given no idea of what work they would have to do, other than 'it will be work on military radios'. The need for secrecy in housing these skilled personnel was also an issue so various large houses in the immediate countryside were requisitioned and converted to hostels.

Cowbridge House had to keep up appearances as a country house estate; packing cases piled outside buildings had to be kept hidden under camouflage netting and reconnaissance aircraft flew over the site regularly to check that there were no tell-tale signs of activity. In June 1940, the 'Top Secret' research and development laboratory, complete with its own workshop was relocated from Southend-on-Sea to Malmesbury. For the sake of secrecy and security it was decided that this needed to be in a completely separate location so vacant shops were acquired in Malmesbury High Street. Behind painted out shop windows, conversion work took place similar to that at Cowbridge House. This unit became known as the WDU (Western Development Unit). Maintaining the secrecy, the selected staff were not told anything until the Friday afternoon before the move. They were sent home and immediately asked to pack for an indefinite period and report back at the works on Sunday morning. They departed in several coaches in convoy, with only the lead coach driver knowing the destination. The staff were only told their final destination once the coach had passed Swindon, some fifteen miles away. These secret laboratories worked under a cover story of being The Ministry of Agriculture and Fisheries. In Malmesbury, the Research & Development staff worked ceaselessly with The Telecommunications Research Establishment (TRE) in refining the design and performance of airborne interception radar. In July 1940, this resulted in the world's first successful radar assisted shoot-down of an enemy aircraft. Unknown at that time it was to change forever the way aerial warfare was waged.

In parallel with developing and manufacturing night fighter radars, EKCO also produced Anti Surface Vessel radar sets for Coastal Command and the Fleet Air Arm where they were instrumental in defeating the U-boat threat. With the invention of the cavity magnetron in 1940, a quantum leap forward in performance was made possible, and night fighters such as the Bristol Beaufighters and the De Havilland Mosquito were soon able to rid Britain's night sky of German bombers. Although too late to be effective during the worst of the Blitz in the winter of 1940/41, they were from 1942 onwards able to take the fight into enemy occupied Europe.

During the war, over 8,500 AI radar sets were manufactured, along with more than 3,000 ASV radar sets during the war, but production continued at Malmesbury as EKCO used their considerable expertise to make military airborne radar units for fighter aircraft such as the Hawker Hunter, they made the ASV radar for Fleet Air Arm Fairey Gannets and in the late 1950's, EKCO also made the tail warning radar for the V-Bomber fleet. With these new advances in technology, EKCO was able to take great strides in developing weather radar, which is arguably one of the biggest steps forward in airliner safety. The first system was reportedly delivered in 1949, although no record remains as to what model the radar was or to whom it was delivered to. In 1952, EKCO won the award to fit weather radar into the new Bristol Britannia's and later in the 1950s into the de Havilland Comet Mark IV's.

In 1959, EKCO developed the world's first 'transistorised' weather radar at Malmesbury, which heralded the golden swansong of radar manufacture, seeing its civilian weather radars selling in large numbers, and ultimately culminated in a radar system being developed and chosen for the Concorde supersonic airliner.

Radar manufacturing ceased in 1960, when all work was transferred to Southend. Malmesbury eventually went over to domestic heating products 'Thermovent,' the EKCO trademark as it became to be known by. Many other products were made at Malmesbury, including inoculating GPO Telephone equipment such as the 'Uniselector' racks. But by this time the company had merged with Pye and Malmesbury was part of the Pye group. Then in the 1970's it reverted back to EKCO Aviation products where the 'Helicopter Attack Radar' was produced under Phil Stride as chief engineer.

Nucleonics

By 1947, the British government had become aware that with the advent of Atomic weapons there was a pressing need to provide the Armed Forces, the Civil Defence, and the Police with some means of detecting radiation in the event of an Atomic/Nuclear explosion. Safe areas with low radiation levels could be marked out and similarly, 'hot spots' of high radiation could be isolated. When the UK's nuclear weapons programme was formally sanctioned in January 1947, it was carried out in parallel with the development of a civil nuclear programme under the Ministry of Supply at Harwell. At that time, the Atomic Energy Research Establishment was still in its embryonic stage and could not handle contracts, so TRE at Malvern became the first Nuclear Instrument Design Authority, since they had the engineering staff and expertise to handle instrument contracts.

EKCO, because of their close ties with TRE and their known expertise, set up a nucleonic laboratory which was staffed by a small group of engineers led by Harold Finch and included Don Smith and Laurie Taylor (to name a few) to work on nucleonic instrumentation research and design (this team later joined by a young Len Lumber). They quickly received a Ministry of Supply contract to manufacture a large number (believed to be a thousand) of portable Dose Rate Meters. These were compact units, a little larger than a brick with, sub-flush handles and controls and the purpose of these meters being that they could measure personal dose rates as well as dose rates of sites and equipment. These meters remained in production for some time and were still being manufactured as late as 1955.

Other Ministry contracts were received for small numbers of laboratory instruments such as Scalers, Counters, Rate Meters, and Amplifiers etc, all of which are remembered well by Charles Exton since he was the chief estimator responsible for negotiation of contract costs with the Technical Cost Branch of the Ministry of Supply at that time.

By the early 1950s, EKCO decided to enter the commercial market with this type of instrumentation and the work of the development group expanded, particularly when Harwell made available commercially produced radioactive isotopes.

There was much pioneering research being done into possible uses of isotopes and applications, which resulted in EKCO designing and manufacturing a range of equipment ranging from detectors to measure material properties, continuous paper thickness measurement at the rolling mills, fluid flow measurement in pipelines, monitoring and controlling 'tape recording' plastic film to measuring the moisture content of tobacco as it was fed into cigarette making machines. In 1956, the decision was made to move all nucleonic activity from Malmesbury to the Nucleonics Service Department at Rochford, where the degree and scope of research, design and manufacture continued to expand. Most of the servicing for EKCO medical instruments was carried out at Rochford, but was transferred to Southend when the site was sold off to the Lesney-Matchbox toy company.

Cowbridge

What was left of the military 'pill boxes' that were used for security outside the main gates disappeared, and the old gazebo at the back of the house, where radar sets were tested was demolished along with the original house. In its place is a housing development of 120 homes. All that remains to mark the site of Malmesbury's once top secret factory is the name of the main road through the new development, 'Sir Bernard Lovell Road'. Named as the pioneer in the development of the radar system which was manufactured at Cowbridge during the war, Sir Bernard (who was knighted in 1961) joined two former shadow workers at the EKCO factory (Marjorie Sandiford and Annie Gilmore) at the road's official opening in November 2009.

Aston Clinton – Wartime Headquarters

Following the evacuation of Southend in June 1940, the village of Aston Clinton in Buckinghamshire became the headquarters of the directors and managers of E K Cole for the duration of the war. The site of the headquarters was in the house and grounds of the Green Park Hotel, which was originally Aston Clinton House, and had been extensively renovated and altered in the 1850's by the Rothschild family, as part of their estates in the area. The house was believed to be the home of Lady Rothschild, and upon her death in 1910 was left to her two daughters who mostly used it as a holiday home. Sometime in the 1930's the house was disposed of and first became the Howard Park Hotel before being renamed the Green Park Hotel, mainly because of the surrounding parkland known as Green Park.

Prior to EKCO moving in, extensive alterations were made to the stable block turning this into laboratories for both radar and communication's research and in another area known as the tower, a small machine shop was set up to make any prototype parts required by the engineers. In the main house, some of the bedrooms were set aside for visiting managers from other sites (such as Malmesbury) while others were used for staff. There were around a hundred EKCO personnel at Aston Clinton, with some of these being locally recruited people. The Green Park Hotel was selected from a short list of potential sites supplied by the Ministry of Aircraft Production and as Derek Cole recounted in his memoirs, a note of high comedy involving his father illuminated the history of this vital move.

"Malmesbury was already working, but much more capacity was needed. Having been given a list of available empty properties, my father set out on a tour of these sites but unknown to him, every ministry was doing the same and unbeknown to him, one of the first sites he enquired at had already been taken over by the Army. As this was at the time that the nation was in a great panic remembering General Franco's claim that he had a 'fifth column' inside Madrid, he was promptly arrested as a spy!

"The result was that a whole day in arranging the move was lost until the village policeman eventually released him. The good thing to come out of this encounter was the fact that my father was then issued with an 'access all areas high level' pass by the ministry, which was to come in handy on more than one occasion."

The first task before anybody could move in was to make the hotel suitable for the influx of the various departments who would move to Aston Clinton, and EKCO's own maintenance department did the majority of this work. The main house did not need much modification apart from some additional electrical sockets and this is where the administration departments set themselves up. As with all the other EKCO sites, the staff at Aston Clinton had to take turns on fire watch duty two nights a week and a watch post was set up on the roof of the building known as the 'tower'. Eric Cole, ever fair to his employees, insisted on doing his turn at fire watching. Should the air raid sirens go, the designated shelter was in the basement/wine cellar. History does not record how well stocked the wine cellar was before or after a raid!

The rules required everybody to move to the cellars when the siren sounded, but as no bombs ever seemed likely to fall in the countryside, over time the staff became somewhat complacent about the rules. This lead one night to a mass refusal to obey the call to go to the cellars, resulting in the manager ringing Cole at home and asking what he should do. Realising this needed his personal attention, Cole wearily struggled into his car and set out. In due course the fire-watchers could see his car travelling along the edge of the Chiltern Hills. Just as it turned down the slope towards Aston Clinton, they heard an aeroplane overhead and then the dread shriek of a falling bomb. To their relief, he drove up to the front door without incident. A few days later a bomb squad dug an unexploded bomb out of the mud in the ditch at the front entrance. Never again was an air raid siren ignored.

Eric Cole rented a house on the outskirts of a nearby village called Great Missenden, and on the night of the invasion scare (7 September 1940) the 'high level - access all areas' pass issued by the Ministry to Cole came in useful when he produced it while, driving home through the Buckinghamshire countryside that night with his wife Muriel and Derek's aunt and uncle in the car.

"Unbeknown to them, because of the invasion scare, all cars were being stopped by the police who were doing identity card checks but when the policeman saw my father's pass, he promptly stepped back, saluted and said, 'You may proceed, Sir, but I should warn you we think German paratroops are landing.'"

Derek's aunt recalled that on arriving home, which had a good line of fire, Eric got out the rifle and shotgun for which he held licences. Derek's uncle (who was called up and trained in 1918 but never reached the front) took the rifle to the back of the house where the field of fire was best, while Cole went to a front window and both their wives stood by as loaders. They stood on watch all that night, but as we know it was a false alarm.

At the administrative headquarters of the company Aston Clinton many technical meetings took place particularly those concerning the re-engineering of TR1154/1155 sets for airborne use. These sets were an original Marconi design that had a steel chassis, whereas the EKCO airborne version had an aluminium chassis for weight saving as well as other modifications, either suggested by EKCO or required by the RAF.

From his office at Aston Clinton, Cole directed the war effort in the various EKCO factory's spread around the country. He later told Derek that his reports went direct to the Minister of Aircraft Production (MAP), and how in the final years of the war, he made frequent visits to Sir Stafford Cripps, later Attlee's 'Iron Chancellor'. Cole was never summoned to No 10, but on occasions Cripps would say, "Winston will want to see this."

Over time Cole and Cripps became good friends, and one by-product of this association was the creation of the Monopolies Commission, after Cole explained he felt that the public had been cheated by the price rigging of the lamp and valve cartels between the wars. Cripps, upon hearing this, apparently went from being the superbly able minister controlling aircraft production to the furiously angry politician. As President of the Board of Trade in the post-war Labour Government, Cripps' first action was the establishment of the Monopolies Commission.

Fortunately, what could have been the most important function of Eric Cole's office at Aston Clinton was never required. His office was designated as the command post for relief efforts if Aylesbury was bombed and, as chairman of the Relief Committee, Cole was appointed to co-ordinate the actions of the Chief Constable, the Fire Chief, the Ambulance Head, the Town Clerk, etc. At the end of the war, Cole decided it was absurd to be given a scroll of honour for services which were not required, and told his son, 'I am not a Boy Scout collecting badges.'

"However, I feel sure that my father regarded his part in the defeat of Hitler the most important thing he ever did."

By 1941, the long hours both overworking and travelling led to Cole having to take enforced time off on doctor's orders, which led to a crisis of confidence in the Ministry of Aircraft Production and bickering amongst the EKCO directors, one of whom was engaged in office politics and is reported to have plotted to remove Cole from the company and take control.

This situation apparently concerned the ministry so much that we now know that consideration was given by the MAP to taking over the company so as to ensure the continuity of supply of both radar and communication equipment such was the vital nature of both products to the war effort. The situation was resolved by the board of directors removing this person who had been a supremely competent (but ambitious) director who had played a major part in EKCO success in the 1930s.

At the end of the war, the Green Park Hotel was handed back to the owners, although the building was demolished in the late 1950s. It was replaced with the Green Park Centre, which is under the control of Buckinghamshire County Council who acquired the property on the proviso that it be used for educational purposes. Many of the original ornamental features of the extended garden were still there as of 2008, but all that remained of the building were the stables.

Demolition of the EKCO Works, Southend, in 2008 (all images P.Brown)

The ageing lighting system in the
underground air raid shelter was still
powered and working in September 2008

Chapter 14

The Tunnels

Even before war broke out, Cole was preparing for the possibility that the factory may be a target for the enemy. Although the Thames Estuary was heavily bombed and EKCO was clearly marked on Luftwaffe maps, the site was never hit; but Cole took no chances. The opportunity was taken between 1938-39, while the works were being enlarged, to excavate the lamp factory and rebuild it incorporating a number of bomb and gas-proof air raid shelters. There was also a high security shelter which could accommodate up to 2,000 people and was capable of withstanding an all but direct hit, used to safeguard the radar and the key design personnel, the engineering personnel and the senior managers and directors of the company.

Whereas standard underground shelters used pre-cast concrete trench-lining, these shelters were formed using concrete pipes measuring two-metre (6ft 6 inch) in inside diameter, the same as those used for large underground waterworks. This meant that it would have been a fairly quick process of dropping each of these pipe sections into the trenches as soon as they were dug.

Concrete steps led down to the shelters, which had heavy steel gauge steel blast and gas proof doors at each end and in the centre to protect the people inside. It was divided into three sections (called galleries), each protected from blast damage in the adjacent gallery by an 'anti-blast' wall as well as the blast doors. Each gallery had two 'Elsan'-type chemical toilets (the same type that was used on the Lancaster bomber) and a clean water supply. Off the central gallery was a separate power room, which was equipped with a diesel engine that drove both a dynamo and an air pump. Air was supplied through the shelter via outlet pipes which had automatic non-return valves in the event of gas contamination. Each shelter had its own power distribution panel where the lighting power could be switched over to an emergency DC power supply from the diesel generator should there be a mains failure or damage caused by enemy action. Behind the power room was a small extension leading to an escape hatch, which in the war years would have indeed have come up in the sports field adjacent to the factory, although with the post-war extension of the roadway this was now in the western roadway.

There was a cleansing station at each entrance to the shelter, where people who had been contaminated with gas would have been treated and washed down prior to going into the shelter. There was also a fully equipped first aid room at the base of north end entrance. Once locked in the tunnels during an air raid, there was no way for the people inside to know when it was over, and so fitted above each exit door was an illuminated sign that warned to 'Stay in shelter until All Clear is sounded,' and had a red and green mica panel which lit up showing the status. This was backed up by a bell system, all of which was operated from above ground. Two further underground shelters were constructed around the same time, and these provided more basic facilities for the production line workers. They lasted a lot longer than anyone could have imagined. As part of the research for this book both authors went on the hunt to find the secret tunnels and in 2008 made several visits to what remained hidden away, and recorded their visits.

Chris Poole:

"With tarmac covering the area behind the main assembly/production hall, any sign of the wooden trap access doors to one of the shelters had gone. However, a chance discussion with an employee of 'Ecomold' (formally EKCO Plastics) who was working in an adjacent (blue) building confirmed that the shelters did in fact exist up to sometime in the early 1980's when a large JCB excavator being used to demolish a redundant building, accidently fell through the cinder surface into part of the underground shelter, which was designed to give quick access to all the workers in that building. It is believed that this shelter could also hold between 500 and 750 people.

"At the time it caused a great deal of hilarity and ribbing, but once the JCB was recovered, the whole surface of the car park was scraped off revealing the network of shelter accommodation below, which was then filled in with rubble, compacted down and then tarmac coated.

"A walk around the site early in 2008 also revealed that one possible surface shelter still existed although the structure had been modified somewhat and the door opening was far too wide, but apart from this, the concrete plinth the brickwork was standing on, along with its concrete roof, were both evidence of a Second World War shelter. The only item missing was the brick wall in front of the entrance, which would have acted as an anti-blast wall protecting the entrance.

Urban myth dispelled

"More than one person had told me that an underground shelter was reputed to exist under or near to the main EKCO office block, with an emergency exit going under the road (Priory Crescent) and coming up in Priory Park, opposite the building. There seemed to be logic here as the directors would have needed a shelter close by, and I was told by one person that this shelter was adjacent to the strong room so that cash, etc, could be secured at short notice. A hunt was subsequently instigated in the old office building before it was demolished, but alas, no evidence whatsoever was found pointing to this shelter, and it was therefore considered to be a bit of an urban myth."

Peter Brown:

"In March 2008, the demolition of the EKCO complex began – a casualty of the changes in law on tax on empty buildings. The site was fenced off as the Kent-based company Downright Demolition Ltd started a nine-month contract to raze the buildings to the ground, and it was while this was going on in May that I arranged through their head office for Chris Poole and myself to have free access to the three large air raid shelters some 20-25 feet underground.

"I phoned Chris that evening, and he was most delighted about the prospect of having access to the tunnels. The next day we met a foreman at the site entrance, who was happy to assist, but insisted that we wore hard boots, hi-visibility vests and hard hats (which we had taken with us in readiness anyway), and his other provision was that we kept clear of the buildings that were actually being demolished. This was the start of what turned out to be a five-month stint of exploration and recording, by notes, photographs and video footage the end of a landmark of Southend's history.'

"We were joined by John Anderson, an IT technician who worked for Ecomold, on our second visit to the shelters, and we continued taking photos, mapping and cataloguing what we found in the great network of tunnels. Following that, Chris invited the curator of Southend Museum to come along, and in the weeks that followed a team from the Archaeological Department from Braintree came down to professionally survey and video the tunnels.

"The shelters were cleared of all their furnishings by the Braintree team, and put into storage for their future display in the new museum planned on the Southend seafront. The only objects they could not remove, because of their sheer weight and size, were the air-tight doors, but I understand that they made a fibreglass cast of one. Some time afterwards, with the demolition and levelling of the site reaching the end, the tunnels were 'sealed' so no-one could gain access to them. It is most likely that the tunnels will never be seen by anyone again.

"The 'safe' on the site, a steel mesh enforced concrete structure (where in most recent times the blank credit cards were stored) presented the demolition crews their biggest problem - it refused to break. Four one-ton Kango-heads had been broken trying to get into it, and so it was decided to leave this until last; it was too time consuming, and would take a cutting crew or explosives to open it.

"One of the Ecomold employees I spoke to in August 2008 told me that he had 21 years under his belt with the company; that when he started there were about 700 employees, and one of their biggest contracts was for British Telecommunications, making their domestic telephones, both the cases and the handsets. There were currently around sixty people left of the workforce, and that as each job came to an end, so ended their employment through redundancy. He anticipated that the company would close down in around four weeks' time, as their insurance was due for renewal in early October."

A last minute reprieve for the site was short lived. The motor giant Ford put in a bid for the foam moulding plant, which was the last remaining operational unit on the site. The method that was used for the production of car bumpers was changing and production would be continued in Europe – the processes used for foam injection moulding in the UK was to be made illegal by 2010, and the company wanted to secure the licenced production there right up to the last minute. However, the bid was turned down by the site developers. What remains on the site now that is the only indication that EKCO even existed are the blue Staffordshire bricks that make up much of the design element of the hexagonal pattern 'floor' between the office building and the pavement of Priory Crescent.

By the end of 2008, the sole remaining building bearing the company's name is the EKCO Social and Sports Club (ESSC) original clubhouse donated by Eric Cole in celebration of the company's Silver Jubilee in 1952. The clubhouse and sports ground were assigned to the ESSC in 'perpetuity',[1]

The EKCO factory site has stood vacant since the buildings were demolished but in recent months has become the focus of the town again as it is being considered as a suitable venue for a hospice for terminally ill patients. It is a suggestion that has greatly pleased Cole family members.

Derek Cole:

"I am particularly anxious that the club and ground should continue. While few in numbers, ex-employees can still be found there discussing times gone by. This is particularly true for the EKCO plastics tool room veterans who still endeavour to meet monthly. I urge Southend Council planners to ensure that this public vital asset remains in place.

"My father always said that EKCO in its days of triumph was an achievement of all the people of Southend.

"His career which began with many innovations for the wireless industry, then contributed strongly to the defeat of Hitler, and in his final post-war years was marked with a passionate devotion to a permanent peace for war-ruined Europe, would be neatly rounded off by the proposed hospice."

---

[1] *It was intended by Eric Cole to grant the clubhouse and sports ground to the ESSC permanently but the law does not permit this. Land can only be passed to a group on a 'trust for sale', with the duty to sell the land and spend the money on the beneficiaries. The Trustees have the power to delay the sale but no more.*

Above: Chris and Margaret Poole (27-10-2006)
Below: Chris and Margaret on their wedding day with bridesmaids and best man
Duncan Cooper at St Mary's Church Prittlewell, Southend-on-Sea.　　　(C.Poole)

Chapter 15

Chris Poole

Christopher Quentin Poole was born in December 1946, at 46 Kings Wall, Malmesbury. He grew up in Bremilham Terrace, Malmesbury, and firstly attended at St Joseph's RC School, Holloway, and then completed his education at Bremilham Secondary Modern School, which was very close to where he lived.

His father Denis and one of their neighbours were 'retained firemen' at the time, and a large bell would ring in the house to alert them of 'a call'; they would both get on their bikes and set off for the fire station at Cross Hayes.

Chris joined EKCO in May 1962 upon leaving school, and served a year working in the main production Auto-Machine Shop, where he learned a lot about Automatic Lathes, Second Operation machines and measurement of components.

In his memories, Chris recalled: "I learnt very quickly the ins and outs of working the system to maximise the piece rate bonuses where each job had an agreed operation time. Work too slowly and not only did you fail to earn a bonus, but you incurred the wrath of the foreman and the girls who had the job timed to perfection. Work too quickly and you ran the risk of the job being re-timed by the 'time and motion' man, with subsequent loss of future bonuses and wrath of the girls (again)."

In May 1963, Chris took up a vacancy in the 'Electronics' Development Inspection Department (which had been moved to larger accommodation at the rear of the original Research & Development building) following a short interview with Roy Henstridge (who was to become his boss), and there started seven and a half years of what Chris later called 'total enjoyment',

The role of the Development Inspection Department was primarily a mechanical inspection of everything made in the 'Model Shop' as well as checking bought in goods, which included electrical components although Ernie's role was checking the prototype wiring looms.

"Since a lot of the parts we were inspecting were development items, when we found faults - sometimes in the drawings themselves, we were expected to liaise with the drawing office and/or the project team rather than just reject the parts. By this means I was able to have what was perhaps a unique insight to the workings of many of the labs and the people working in them."

The development projects Chris handled included the E-190 Gearbox and Scanner Unit - the smallest weather radar of the EKCO family developed in the mid 60's to meet the needs of the new generation of 'light twins' such as the Piper Aztec, the Beech Queen Air and the Beagle 206, which were becoming popular in private ownership towards the end of the 1960s). Other projects included the helicopter radar ARI 5955, and the E-390 radar system developed for Boeing 747s and Concorde.

"One of the most frightening duties I had was using the 'Magnetiser' which was a device designed by John Yarrow and used for imparting a high magnetic field into the soft iron blocks moulded into various components. It was frightening insofar as this piece of equipment was in its own room adjacent to George 'Gibby' Gibson (the Chief Mechanical Engineer)'s lab and I had strict instructions to remove any metallic objects, including my watch before entering the room and switching on. I swear that when the 'Magnetiser' was switched on the lights dimmed and it emitted an ominous hum akin to the sort of noise heard in the Frankenstein movies. I don't know what the power consumption was but by the size of the power leads it must have been considerable. Suffice to say that using the machine was not popular and I did sometimes wonder about the highly magnetic environment.

"In my travels, I used to visit Pat Heath's lab and remember this was a place where there was always a convivial atmosphere and I have two abiding memories. The first is Bob Puttock's calculation for working out the changes in wave-guide propagation through the droop snoot of Concorde. This was I know considered a 'tour-de-force' at the time since all the calculation was done long hand with only a slide rule for help and for a long time I remembered it stayed on their large black-board.

"The second abiding memory is the seemingly casual way they used to heat up pies and sausage rolls etc by pointing a wave-guide horn at the food - this some twenty years before microwave ovens became popular.

"I worked in the Environmental Test Lab. What was fascinating about this lab was the fact that it was equipped with two large vibration tables (made by Ling I think?) upon which a scanner unit or a T/R unit could be mounted and vibrated over a wide vibration range going down I think to 20Hz. The object of this testing was to simulate the vibration regime of the aircraft or helicopter. I recall that one of the party tricks to demonstrate the equipment to important visitors was to take a TV from the main production line and watch it self-destruct in a very short time. One of the big concerns about the building being where it was the fact that the vibrations would transmit through the foundations or the roof and affect the adjacent engineering tower block, and cracks certainly did appear in this building, with plaster and brick dust known to fall onto drawing boards in the office on the top floor."

The Scrap Chit

"With security staff on the front and rear entrances (they never apparently twigged that you could leave through the gate from the sports field) to take anything off the site you had to have a chit. Of course this was only used for objects which would not fit into pockets (valves and small components such as resistors etc. were considered fair game and worth the risk of getting stopped for a random check) but by the mid-1960's the top of the range TV cases were still made of mahogany or if it was a Dynatron even teak.

"The net result of this was many of the staff sought out scrap television cases from the 'Willow Run', which were taken home and used to make coffee tables, for example. The procedure was that you should take the piece of wood you wanted to the 'Scrap Officer' who worked upstairs above Personnel and he would evaluate the piece and issue a scrap chit upon payment of a small sum such as sixpence (6d) or one shilling in old money and it was not unknown for the teak pieces to be up to 5 shillings if it was from a large 24 or 26 inch cabinet.

"Of course everybody soon wised up to this with the result that many departments had a suitably badly scratched piece of wooden cabinet, which was taken to the Scrap Officer whenever you found a good piece of wood. We used to have bets on how much he would charge and never ceased to be amazed by the variation in price for the same piece of scrap wood.

"I became involved with the Southend site through recording my own father's story - he was an instrument maker at Malmesbury, building scanner units, and when work was transferred to Southend in late 1960, we as a family moved to Southend. I worked in the Development Inspection Department until the whole thing closed in 1971, although my father then moved to MEL Crawley to help them set up the radar build line there."

Chris was made redundant on 4 December 1970. In the decades that followed Chris collated stories of others who worked alongside him and at other EKCO factories throughout the company's history. He documented products and components and even set up and run a website about EKCO which was used by many historians and enthusiasts as a veritable archive.

~~~~~~~~~~~~~~~~~~~~~~

Publisher's note:

"When I met Chris his health was failing but it was abundantly clear how much passion he had for telling the story of EKCO. Sadly, Chris passed away on 9th October 2012, without seeing his life's endeavour in print but he died knowing it would be published.

"He leaves a lasting legacy for the people of Southend and for the world to truly understand how a humble radio producing factory on the outskirts of Southend-on-Sea really did change the world."

Above: Denis Poole, Chris' father, working the E-390 radar system developed for Boeing 747s and Concorde.　　(All images C.Poole)

Chris Poole (1946-2012)

Appendix 1

Roll Call of No 9 (EKCO) Platoon

The platoon was split up into four sections, namely the HQ section, the Vickers Machine Gun section, the Spigot Mortar (bombard) section, and an 'other ranks' General Duties section. The HQ section had four sub-sections, namely the Watch, Stores, Clerical Staff, and Supernumeraries.

The Vickers Gun section was under the command of Sergeant P M Stiddig and split into three teams of four people, each lead by a Lance Corporal - L/Cpl A Allsop with 'A' team, L/Cpl H Wood with 'B' team, and L/Cpl C Higgs with 'C' team.

The EKCO Spigot Mortar section, formed in 1942, consisted of sixteen men who were split into four teams; Bombard 'L' - subsection, Bombard 'M' - subsection, Bombard 'N' - subsection and Bombard 'O' - subsection.

The General Duties section was subdivided into four subsections, which themselves were made up of three teams. The subsections were identified as Section 33 (Commander Sergeant J H Endruweit); Section 34 (Commander Sergeant R C Smart); Section 35 (Commander Sergeant G A Richardson), and Section 36 (Commander Sergeant A White).

Each of the four subsections nominally comprised of 25 men. It is believed that two Spigot Mortars were allocated to this section together with 150 rounds of 20lb (anti-tank) and 100 rounds of 14lb (anti-personnel) ammunition as this was very much the general issue across the Southern Command Home Guard at that time.

The known list of names in No 9 Platoon in alphabetical order as of March 1942

Abbott H	Chinn	Giggins	Martin K	Smith W
Adams	Christie F	Gilber	Maskell B	Stonham C
Alderton R	Chrystal A	Glenister A	Matthews G	Stevens R E
Allsop A	Clements S	Golding W	Matthews S	Swift W
Ayling F	Coe	Grimwade	McGrath J	Tavener D
Bailey	Comte	Halliday J	Merrill L	Taylor
Baker	Conley	Hasler E T	Minney	Taylor
Baker	Conquest F	Hendy A	Minney	Thomas R
Balmer G	Cox	Herit	North A J	Thorndycraft H
Barlow	Cox T	Higgs C	Owen C	Thurlow
Barlow J	Cox W	Hill L	Pace M	Tomlin J
Bassett	Cundey A	Hill S	Parry C	Trumble C
Beale A	Currie H	Hobbs D	Pennac	Vousden E
Beard	Craig J S	Holden	Perry C	Warwick K
Beeton	Crocker C	Hooker	Plumstead L	Weller W
Bennett A	Dansie T	Hooker D	Potter R	Went J
Bennett H	Deer P	Humphries	Pritchett S	White
Bennett L	Dicken	Hurley A	Richardson	White E
Bradford S	Dixon	Hyma	Sabine	Wolfe E
Bradley	Elliott G	Izod L	Savory W	Wood H
Bright	Endruweit J	Jeffery F	Scraggs S	Wood H
Brooks W	Evans A	Johnson D	Sheperd E	Woodward T
Brown A	Evans J	Johnson H	Sherringham	Woodward
Busby A	Faithfull	Kinnerman	Sittenbaum	Wright W
Busby G F M	Fairchild L	Ladd C J	Sponder F	Young
Chandler D	Fisher R	Langridge	Smart F	Yorwarth F
Chandler L	Fisher R J	Lawrence W	Smart R	
Chapman J	Fitch L E	Le Bon E	Smith A	
Chapple	Flowers C	Lee S	Smith A	
Childs G	Fudge C	Linklater P	Smith H	

Note: In April 1942, another nine men were added: Ambler G C, Bradley R, Callow F,

Appendix 2

Company structure in January 1960

The following information, which was released internally in January 1960, reveals the size and scope of the company. Listed below are the directors, the subsidiary companies, the associate companies, the market sectors the business was operating in, the premises, and the number of personnel employed at each site.

<u>UK Principal Market Sectors (January 1960)</u>

E.K. Cole Ltd (EKCO)
Ekcovision
EKCO Radio and Car Radio
EKCO Domestic and Industrial Heating Equipment

EKCO Plastics Ltd.
Injection, Compression and Vacuum formed Mouldings for Industry,
EKCO 'Gold Seal' Domestic Ware

EKCO Electronics Ltd.
Electronic, Nucleonic, Radar and V.H.F. Equipment

Ferranti Radio and Television Ltd.
Television and Radio

Dynatron Radio Ltd.
Television, Radio, Radiograms, Electronic and Nucleonic Equipment

Egen Electronic Ltd.
Television, Electronic and Radio Components.

The Warmglow Co. Ltd.
Electric Blankets and Electrical Equipment.

Subsidiary Companies

American Tradair Corporation – New York
Dynatron Radio Ltd.
Egen Electric Ltd.
EKCO Electronics Ltd.
EKCO Plastics Ltd.
Ferranti Radio & Television Ltd.
The Warmglow Co. Ltd.

Associate Companies

E.K. Cole (Colombia) Ltda. – Bogotá
Ediswan-EKCO (Aust.) Pty. Ltd.
EKCO-Ensign Electric Ltd.
Kelly & Shiel (EKCO Products) Ltd. – Dublin
Kruger-Wilson Africa Ltd. – Johannesburg
The National EKCO Radio & Engineering Co. Ltd. – Bombay
The Ultimate-EKCO (NZ) Co. Ltd. – Auckland

Various premises of the EKCO company (January 1960)

E K Cole Ltd EKCO Works, Priory Crescent, Southend on Sea, Essex (HQ)
Dynatron Radio Ltd. St. Peters Road, Furze Platt, Maidenhead, Berks
Egen Electric Ltd. Charfleet Industrial Estate, Canvey Island, Essex
Ferranti Radio & Television Ltd. 41-47 Old Street, London EC1
The Warmglow Co. Ltd. Progress Road, Leigh-on-Sea, Essex

Branch Offices: London office and showrooms: 5 Vigo Street, London W1

Service Headquarters: Somerton Works, Arterial Rd. Westcliff-on-Sea, Essex

Service Depots & Showrooms:
115 Jersey Street, Ancoats, Manchester 4
230/2 Highgate Road, Birmingham 12
17 Cadogan Street, Glasgow C2

UK Manufacturing site data as at January 1960

Factory	Site Area	Cover Floor Area	Number of Employee's
Southend	19 Acres	506,000 sq.ft.	5,512**
Malmesbury	10 Acres	80,000 sq.ft.	742
Kenway	3 ¼ Acres	30,700 sq.ft.	679**
Maidenhead	3 Acres	40,000 sq.ft	390
Canvey	1 1/3 Acres	19,300 sq.ft.	344
Progress Rd.	1 Acre	13,800 sq.ft	74
Somerton	½ Acre	16,600 sq.ft.	145
Hadleigh	1/7th Acre	5,400 sq.ft.	83

**Note: It is believed that these total employee counts were provided by the Personnel Department. There is some considerable doubt about the accuracy of these figures, which almost certainly overstates the numbers since 3,500 is considered a more realistic number at Priory Park and no more than 300 at Kenway.

Board of Directors

Eric K Cole CBE	**Chairman and Managing Director**
E R Pring	
E B Willcocks	Director and Secretary
J Corbishley	Director and Finance Controller
A W Martin MBE	Technical Director
W M York	Commercial Director

Executive Directors

G W Godfrey	Executive Director – Radio Sales
D Radford	Executive Director & General Manager – EKCO Plastics
A J Brunker	Executive Director & Chief Engineer
S A Clodd	Executive Director & Works Manager